W9-BTI-711

WITHDRAWN
NDSU

MATHEMATICAL MODELS OF ECONOMIC GROWTH

ECONOMICS HANDBOOK SERIES

SEYMOUR E. HARRIS, EDITOR

ADVISORY COMMITTEE: Edward H. Chamberlain, Gottfried Haberler, Alvin H. Hansen, Edward S. Mason, and John H. Williams. *All of Harvard University.*

Burns · SOCIAL SECURITY AND PUBLIC POLICY
Duesenberry · BUSINESS CYCLES AND ECONOMIC GROWTH
Hansen · A GUIDE TO KEYNES
Hansen · ECONOMIC ISSUES OF THE 1960S
Hansen · MONETARY THEORY AND FISCAL POLICY
Hansen · THE AMERICAN ECONOMY
Harris · INTERNATIONAL AND INTERREGIONAL ECONOMICS
Henderson and Quandt · MICROECONOMIC THEORY
Hoover · THE LOCATION OF ECONOMIC ACTIVITY
Johnston · STATISTICAL COST ANALYSIS
Kindleberger · ECONOMIC DEVELOPMENT
Lerner · ECONOMICS OF EMPLOYMENT
Taylor · A HISTORY OF ECONOMIC THOUGHT
Tinbergen and Bos · MATHEMATICAL MODELS OF ECONOMIC GROWTH
Valavanis · ECONOMETRICS

MATHEMATICAL MODELS OF ECONOMIC GROWTH

Jan Tinbergen

PROFESSOR OF DEVELOPMENT PROGRAMMING
NETHERLANDS SCHOOL OF ECONOMICS

Hendricus C. Bos

SENIOR RESEARCH FELLOW
NETHERLANDS SCHOOL OF ECONOMICS

McGRAW-HILL BOOK COMPANY, INC. 1962

New York San Francisco Toronto London

148364

MATHEMATICAL MODELS OF ECONOMIC GROWTH

Copyright © 1962 by the McGraw-Hill Book Company, Inc. Printed in the United States of America. All rights reserved. This book, or parts thereof, may not be reproduced in any form without permission of the publishers. *Library of Congress Catalog Card Number* 61-13760

64901 THE MAPLE PRESS COMPANY, YORK, PA.

HB
71
T5

PREFACE

We hope this book will be useful to civil servants in charge of development planning as well as to future planners during their university education. It tries to provide building blocks rather than a completed building. A number of features characteristic of development programs are dealt with in a systematic way. The expository principle underlying the book, whereby each feature is presented in the simplest conceivable way, is due to the great master of one of us, Paul Ehrenfest.

The book uses mathematics, since we think the subject requires it. The mathematics used are modest, however, and within reach of those who have followed calculus and algebra courses, with some slight extensions which can be mastered for the purpose without much trouble. The emphasis is on the economic significance of the subject matter.

The choice of the models treated is not arbitrary, but in our opinion represents the main contribution we have to offer. We have deliberately left out some approaches, well known from theoretical literature, which we think are not of much practical value. To be sure the reverse is not true: we have indulged in a few topics which are not practically applicable either, but which are thought to contribute to understanding.

We are aware of our own limitations and shall welcome any comments our readers may care to make.

Jan Tinbergen
Hendricus C. Bos

CONTENTS

Chapter 1

INTRODUCTORY; USE OF MATHEMATICAL MODELS

1.1. Aims and Means of Development Policies

1.11 In this book a number of mathematical models will be discussed which may be helpful to the design of development policy and more particularly to development planning. An increasing number of countries—both underdeveloped and developed—are pursuing a conscious policy of furthering development nowadays. This justifies a closer study of the mechanism of development with a view to finding optimum policies. For a proper understanding of the subject matter, some remarks must first be made about the nature of the problems and phenomena involved.

It is useful to distinguish between two broad classes of problems, sometimes called analytical and policy problems. Analytical problems, in this context, are the usual problems of economic analysis, whose objective is to explain the course of economic variables when a number of *data* are given. These data are, on the one hand, phenomena of an extraeconomic character, that is, natural, psychological, technical, or institutional phenomena. On the other hand, they may be economic phenomena or variables outside the geographical area considered—usually a country. The data can be such things as crop yields, tastes of the population, technological coefficients, or tax rates. An important subdivision of the category of data in the context of our problem is that which can be influenced by government policy, to be called *means* or *instruments of economic policy*, and data which cannot be influenced. Policy problems, in our context, are problems in which the logic of analytical problems is partly inverted. Those data which are means or instruments of economic policy are no longer considered as given, but rather as unknowns. Inversely, some things are supposed known about the economic variables which are the unknowns in analytical problems. Assumed known are the *aims* of the policy considered; that is, either the precise values of some variables, to be called *target variables*, must be given or some function of them, to be called *social welfare function* or *social utility function*, must be a maximum. Thus, in development policy it may be that some fixed targets are set—a 20 per cent rise in national income and a 10 per cent rise in employment, say—or that the government aims at an optimum combination of national income, employment, and regional income distribution. The former type of problem, characterized by a set of fixed targets, requires that the number of instruments used be at least equal to the number of targets. There is less of such a condition in the case of the latter type of problem, but there must be at least 1 *degree of freedom*, that is, something to choose; otherwise nothing can be made a maximum.

1.12 Although models can be used for the solution of analytical problems as well as of policy problems, the emphasis in this book will be on their use in the solution of policy problems. One model can be used for the solution of a large number of different policy problems, however, and what we are going to say of these problems illustrates our main subject only. This book is not dealing with development policy in the first place, but with models that can be used in designing such a policy. Even so it is proper to say something about the aims and means which most frequently characterize development policy. We have seen already that such aims may be given the shape of fixed targets or of something more flexible, where a certain welfare function must be made a maximum. In fact there is no contradiction between these two ways of putting things. In principle the fixed targets should be chosen so as to lead to maximum welfare; they often represent what the policy maker intuitively thinks will maximize welfare. It is more correct, from a scientific point of view, not to consider them as given beforehand, that is, independently of the operation of the economic mechanism and more particularly independently of the instruments chosen. In fact they will often have been chosen on the basis of considerable knowledge with regard to these things. For practical purposes the setting of fixed targets is often attractive, especially for short-run policy problems. This is so because not much definite can be said about the shape of the social welfare function, meaning that the scientific adviser cannot easily replace the intuitive choice of the policy maker by something more precise. He can, however, with some reasonable accuracy, derive statements about the instrument values that will bring about a certain set of target values in a given economy.

In a more scientific treatment of problems of development policy it does make sense, however, to say something about the maximization process behind the choice of targets, especially if long-term targets are considered. Even if important clues for practical action cannot yet be derived, some clarification about the logical structure of the problems at stake can be obtained.

The most general way of putting the problem of long-term development policy is to say that total welfare or social utility over a long period should be maximized, in principle even an infinitely long period. This welfare is dependent on a number of economic variables for all time units in the period. Among these variables, consumption stands out, but distribution of consumption over regions or groups, and variables like employment, as well as others, will also influence welfare. The problem therefore necessarily is a very complicated one, and the planner may have considerable need for simplification.

One important method of simplifying the solution of the problem is to break it down into steps or *stages*, which can be tackled in succession. More specifically, for development planning it seems appropriate first to deal with the problem of distributing consumption over time without entering into the composition with regard to individual commodities, and next to deal with the composition. This means that first a macroproblem is set in which the intricacies of distribution over time are given full attention, and that as a second stage a microproblem is solved. More precisely, the microproblem itself may be considered in a succession of stages, each referring to the proper allocation of investment between industries in a single year.

To be sure, the procedure may well be incorrect, and it has to be proved that, as a first approximation, it can be accepted. The authors believe that this proof is possible.

Other methods of simplification are to be found in the *choice of the variables*. Thus, consumption only, as the main variable, may be assumed to determine welfare. As a second approximation, one of the other variables only may be added, for example, employment. Instead of maximizing consumption over a long period, in certain circumstances, income may be maximized, where the amount spent on investment stands for additional consumption later.

1.13 The means of development policy applied in different countries depend very much on the preferences of their governments with regard to the *economic order*. In communist countries, where a much larger portion of the means of production is publicly owned, a much larger number of means of policy are available than in noncommunist countries. It would be inexact to say that all acts of the managers of publicly owned production units are themselves means of economic policy, since not all these acts can be controlled by the government. But clearly the grip of the government on such decisions is much tighter than in the case of privately owned production units. As a first approximation it may be said that investments in all industries in the public sectors are instruments of policy, and these are less numerous, although by no means unimportant, in noncommunist countries. Further important instruments are the other well-known instruments of public finance, that is, public expenditure for other than investment purposes, taxes, and subsidies.

In most, though not all, communist and in some other countries, prices are an instrument of policy, including the "prices" of labor, wage rates, and the "prices" of capital, interest rates.

In smaller countries the instruments of trade policy (duties and quantitative restrictions) have a considerable impact on the economy.

1.14 Planning, or programming, of development is an activity which to a considerable extent is independent of the precise development policy pursued by a government, that is, independent of the means applied in such policy. Even a policy that relies only on indirect ways to influence production may be well served by advance planning that charts the most desirable course of production and its components. This is true wherever complicated and time-consuming processes are involved: inconsistencies can be at least partly avoided by advance planning.

Planning differs from pure forecasting in that it is based on the assumption that the future course of production and other economic variables can be influenced, and it aims at indicating the most desirable course. What constitutes the most desirable course depends very much, however, on the aims set and the means to be admitted.

Historically the desirability of planning has become clear because of the inconsistencies that may exist among measures designed by various ministries or departments and divisions if those measures are based on a partial analysis only. The assumptions made by an electricity board may be incompatible with those made by a department of agriculture or a board of trade.

Planning is an almost continuous process. At regular, fairly short intervals, plans have to be revised in the light of new information. This new information may consist of figures about external data of a random character such as crops or about systematic changes in the other data; it may consist also of figures about the economic variables which have materialized meanwhile and which may deviate from those expected, first, because the data deviated from expectations and, second, because the relationships assumed are different from the real relationships.

1.2. Mathematical Models as a Hard Core of Programming

1.21 Programming of development requires a number of different abilities and types of knowledge. As a rule the process consists in estimating such a large number of figures that first of all considerable organizing abilities are needed. The way in which the large number of people necessarily involved in the process cooperate and the way their various acts succeed each other and fit into the general pattern are by no means arbitrary or unimportant. It is a common misunderstanding that activities can simply start at the bottom of the pyramid of agencies and that the coordinating role of the center comes in later. There is a certain optimum degree of centralized directives to be emitted first, so as to avoid the most primitive inconsistencies in the work done by the base. This example may illustrate the role of organization. Its role is also very important because an essential feature of efficient planning consists in planning in as short a time as possible.

But the work proper of calculating the figures also requires a number of different abilities, mostly not present in one single man. It requires, in other words, the cooperation of a large number of specialists, first of all, specialists in various technological fields. This is particularly true for the appraisal of investment projects in many different sectors. It is true also, but to a lower degree, for the estimation of future demand, if this is to a high degree dependent on technical development. Then, specialists in the economic field are needed, vested with knowledge of the prospects and peculiarities of a number of markets. They have to take care of the estimation of exports in the first place, but also of home sales. They often need the help of statisticians and econometrists. In the third place, specialists in the broader field of sociology and psychology have to play their part, more particularly if industrialization is extended to new areas, and if the way of life of formerly rural people is involved. Social and political experts may also be useful to judge the priorities in these fields when it comes to changing social insurance, wage systems, industrial democracy, and tax systems.

Finally there is a special role for those economists whom we nowadays call macroeconomists.

1.22 The task of macroeconomists is the one of coordinating much of the work done by the other experts, but not coordinating it in the sense of organizing it. The coordination meant here is of a more abstract nature. The macroeconomists have to see to it that no inconsistencies creep into the system of figures which ultimately constitute the plan.

In principle there is only one way to take care of this task; in practice there are more, since we have to work with approximations and trial-and-error procedures. In order, however, to give at least a sharp theoretical description of the task, let us take the ideal method for a while. It is essentially of a mathematical or, if that term is preferred, of a logical character. The complete operation, in all its details, of an economy and the human beings populating it can be described by a mathematical model of a much more complicated and sophisticated nature than anything we know in reality. To deny this is equivalent to denying the possibility of the scientific treatment of the operation of society. It does not imply the assumption of determinacy in the old sense, since we have the tool of stochastic variables, representing—in physics as well as economics, to cite only two examples—those elements of "freedom" sometimes invoked against the assumption of determinacy. The essence of a model is precisely that of an orderly and, in a sense, complete administration of knowledge. It is for this reason that the model supplies us with the tools of coordination.

A model consists of a number of elements, now to be considered from the formal side only. The economic contents will be discussed in Sec. 1.5. A model consists of (1) a list of variables, to be subdivided into known and unknown or exogenous and endogenous variables in the analytical sense used above; and (2) a list of relationships or equations specifying the links of any type that exist between the variables, to be subdivided into definitions, balance equations, technological and institutional equations, and behavior equations. Each equation represents a set of *links* or *reactions* with a causal direction, sometimes symbolized by arrows directed toward the variable affected. The links represented in one equation are those meeting in one variable at one point of time and together responsible for the size that variable will take at that time. In each equation, therefore, those variables occur which influence the variable in which the links meet. There are other elements too in the equations, representing a third element of the model: (3) coefficients. They describe the intensity with which one variable affects, through one particular link, another variable. (Additive constants will be considered coefficients too.) They are typical of what is sometimes called the structure of the mechanism or organism.

The elements of a hypothetical ideal model of society can be used to analyze the process of planning and the coordinating task of the macroeconomist in it.

1.23 The figures which ultimately are to form the plan are the values of a number of the variables, more particularly the endogenous variables of the model. These variables are the outcome or, mathematically speaking, the solutions of the system of equations, given the exogenous variables, some of the endogenous variables at earlier time periods, and the coefficients. Since, in principle, they are interdependent, it cannot be that the variables referring to the agricultural sector are calculated by the agricultural experts, those of the textile sector by the textile experts, and so on. They can be calculated only by one man who solves the system of equations, perhaps helped by a machine.

This does not mean, fortunately, that this man has to unite in himself all the knowledge incorporated in the whole model. Both other elements, the equations and the coefficients, can be established one by one, and open up the possibility of decentralization and specialization of jobs. Also, the choice of variables that should be included in the list is a matter that can be decided upon in a joint discussion. The establishment of an equation describing the supply of agricultural products—or of one of them—not only can be left to the agricultural specialist, but definitely should be undertaken by him. Similarly, the establishment of other relations must be the task of other specialists. In the light of modern statistical methods, our statement has to be qualified: the choice of the variables and the mathematical shape of each equation are typically the tasks of the specialist in the field concerned. The actual determination of the coefficients may sometimes be a problem requiring centralized work. Yet the so-called a priori estimation of coefficients as well as the judgment of coefficients obtained by a centralized simultaneous-equations approach is profitably left to the specialist.

This, then, would constitute a reasonable division of labor between the coordinating macroeconomist and the specialists: the list of variables to be included should be based on suggestions from all specialists, discussed together; nature of equations and variables to be included, a priori estimation of coefficients, and a posteriori judgment of coefficients determined by simultaneous-equations method are tasks of the specialists, each in his own field; simultaneous determination of coefficients, as far as necessary, and the solution of the system of equations are typically the tasks of the macroeconomist. The latter is a specialist not in any material field but in interdependency problems.

1.24 It is the contention of the authors that this task, in fact, and not only in theory, can best be accomplished with the aid of a mathematical model. It does not follow from this statement that it could not be done otherwise. In fact, most development plans have been made without such a model, by methods of trial and error at different levels. Nor is it the opinion of the authors that the coordinating macroeconomist should aim at establishing this ideal model, which was the basis of their reconnaissance-in-principle, at least not in the short run. As will be set out in Sec. 1.4, the authors are in favor of approximative methods to be called *planning in stages*.

Yet the authors feel that the core of a development plan should be formed by some type of mathematical model. Such a model, or a combination of them for various stages, has clear advantages typical of systematic treatment. Outstanding general advantages are clarity and consistency, that is, the avoidance of inner contradictions. But there are more. As already set out in the previous subsection, a mathematical treatment yields a natural subdivision of the work into well-defined separate tasks that can be tackled in succession. In addition, a mathematical treatment offers some of the advantages of roundabout production: at relatively little extra cost, alternative calculations can be made which enable us to judge at least some of the *confidence intervals* or *limits of reliability* and to judge the effects of alternative policies.

1.3. Conditions of Practical Applicability

1.31 The mathematical models to be used in development programming and to be discussed in this book have to satisfy a number of conditions which distinguish them from the vaster category of all conceivable models and which limit the degree of their complexity. They must be applied practically, "here and now," above all in underdeveloped countries. It is perhaps not each of the conditions separately but the combination of them that sometimes causes much trouble or limits their scope. Therefore, it goes without saying that the models to be used must be *complete* in the sense that they cover the whole economy and do not overlook phenomena of vital importance. They must be *correct* also in that they use coefficients which are in reasonable agreement with reality. By themselves these conditions are self-evident and common to all serious models. It is the combination with other conditions which we must now discuss.

1.32 The coefficients we are using must be more or less known, that is, no extensive or novel research, not yet generally recognized as pertinent, must be needed to determine the coefficients. Some of the more theoretical models presented in recent theoretical literature contain a host of relations of which we have not the slightest knowledge. Such models must be excluded from a practical program and from this book. Of course, work on them must go on in the universities and research institutes. These models may bring out features of vital importance which we are not yet aware of. It may well be that some of our policies of today will have no success because we did not know enough about these features. But we cannot base calculations on unknown relations.

1.33 Another condition our models must satisfy is that they must be manageable, and, more particularly, manageable by those who have to handle them. In part this is a question of the quality of the staff available to planning agencies. The models should not be too difficult and too elaborate. Both terms are very vague, to be sure, and leave much to the question of taste. We do not believe in models with hundreds of variables, at least for the time being. For the rest, it depends on the country concerned; some of our models may be useful to the more advanced only, others to a large number of less advanced countries—in the sense of having less specialized planners.

1.34 To a certain extent the models must also be understandable to those who have to use the results of planning. This is even more vague an idea than the one of manageability. Almost none of the models here presented will appeal as such to the politicians whom they have to serve. They will have to be explained to them by the planners. Much will depend then on the didactic abilities of the latter. The general tendency of this part of the argument imposes a further restriction on the use of complicated concepts. What matters more perhaps is that no model should be made unnecessarily complicated. Often there are elegant ways of representing the main features of a mechanism or organism in a relatively simple way. In modern economic language our recommendations are: never use unnecessary boundary conditions or unnecessary input-output relations.

The choice of the proper model in any situation remains very much a question of taste. In a way, therefore, the reader will have to have a look at our collection of models in order to find out what we mean by the preceding conditions. The proof of the pudding is in the eating.

1.4. Successive Approximations as a Method

1.41 As has been said in the preceding sections (see Sec. 1.24), we are in favor of a method of development programming to be called *planning in stages*, which stands at variance with the more ambitious method of establishing one very complicated model for a simultaneous solution of all problems. In a general way, planning in stages is an attempt first to determine a few of the most important ("strategic") variables and later to determine others, thus coming to greater detail and gradually covering a longer period. Before going into some of the concrete features of the method, we may present a general argument in favor of it. The method is a special case of the well-known and old mathematical—and general scientific—method of successive approximations (or "decreasing abstraction"). This latter constitutes not only a semiscientific procedure for purely applied calculations but also, in many cases for lack of better, the only way out for scientific research. This is true in such cases where a more direct or precise method does not or does not yet exist. Since in many cases the accuracy of the approximative method can be increased at will, it can be used in general proofs of scientific statements. Its scientific "rank" should not therefore be misunderstood.

1.42 What matters more for the practice of planning, however, is that in order to reach a certain numerical result the method of successive approximations often requires less effort than the exact method, where it exists. In practice, numerical results need not be absolutely exact, but have to have only a margin of error below a certain prescribed limit. Thus, if we have to calculate the figure 1.003^4 up to three decimal places, there is no need of the complete "correct" calculation; the approximative answer $1 + 4 \times 0.003 = 1.012$ suffices. The gain of time and effort is considerable. As is well known, development in power series is a general and frequently used device to which the preceding remarks apply.

1.43 A few remarks may be added already on the concrete *stages of development planning* which we recommend. More will be said in Chap. 8, after the techniques have been discussed.

As a rule the first stage may consist of a macroeconomic study of the general process of production and investment, along the lines suggested by Harrod-Domar models or by similar, somewhat more complicated models. The aim of this first stage should be to determine, in a provisional way, the rate of savings and the general index of production. A second stage may consist then in specifying production targets for a number of sectors over a fairly long period. A third stage, if needed, may go into more detail for a shorter period, giving figures for a larger number of smaller sectors. A fourth stage may consist in "filling the plan out" with individual projects. Intermixed with this succession there may be stages of revision of the previous stages. Thus, the figures of the second stage may already enable the planner to revise some of the coefficients used in the first stage and to re-do, therefore, the first stage. After a fixed interval of time, new data will be available and this may lead to another revision, combined or not with shifting the period of the plan.

1.44 This was an example only. Other stages may be called for by the situation. There is no need for fixed rules; adaptability is one of the virtues of the planner. In a slightly different sense, "stages" come in also by what could be called "partial" models, designed to highlight a detail. Market analyses for separate export products, especially the smaller ones, are good examples. So are models about locations conditions in some big individual project.

1.5. Main Elements of Models

1.51 The models to be discussed in this book have been selected with a view to the purposes they must serve and to the conditions discussed in the preceding section. They have been selected to give a picture of the process of development, above all, and to meet the needs of planners for development. As economic models they emphasize the phenomena of production in the first place, that is, the material side of the phenomenon of development. The side of training and education has been disregarded; it is assumed that the problems in that realm will be solved.

Accordingly, the two basic phenomena to be found in the models are those of the factors of production and of products. Among the factors of production only the scarcest have been considered: very often only capital is considered; sometimes capital and labor are both considered. Land does not need so much attention in a study of development, which is essentially a process in time, because in time the quantity of land proper hardly changes.

Central importance for the production and development processes must be attached to the relationship between the quantity of product and the quantities of production factors used, the production function. In most models the production function has been assumed to be one of proportionality between inputs and outputs, which in its simplest form—with capital the only production factor—comes to the assumption of a constant capital coefficient. In some of our models more complicated relationships have been assumed, for example, the well-known Cobb-Douglas function.

1.52 For planning purposes it is often desirable to distinguish a number of different industries or processes, corresponding with different products. We shall speak of different *sectors* in this context, a sector being characterized not only by the figures for production, but also by the figures for imports and exports of the same product and by the figures for the uses made of the product, that is, final consumption, investment, or use as an input in current production of some other product.

The number of sectors will be assumed to be large in several models, and simple methods are discussed for dealing with such models. The number of producing sectors will sometimes also be assumed to be changing, which seems a natural thing for the process of development. A sector without production—but possibly with all other items except exports—will be called an *empty* sector. A sector without foreign trade will be called a *national* sector. In models showing a number of regions as parts of a national economy, sectors without interregional flows will be called *regional* sectors.

1.53 Since the phenomenon of *investment* is crucial to the process of development, no model will be without this economic variable. In many models, however, investment goods will not be distinguished from consumer goods, meaning that a commodity can be used either way. If stock accumulation of goods of any kind is considered investment, this is only natural. We shall discuss models with only one sector as well as models with many sectors where the assumption just formulated is made. We shall also discuss, however, models in which investment goods are a different type of goods not used for consumption purposes. As the simplest case, we consider, in this class, a model with only one capital good. This is permitted, of course, only if no appreciable differences in price development among different capital goods need be assumed to exist and if no import difficulties occur with some types of capital goods, while not occurring with other types. The *specificity* of capital goods can be carried one step further by distinguishing between capital goods of the first and of higher orders, as will be done in a few models.

In the process of investment a vital role is played by the *capital-output ratio*, as already observed. This will be assumed to be different for different sectors as a rule; it is interesting to note, however, that, if capital were the only scarce factor of production, prices of the various products would tend to equalize capital-output ratios. Assuming different capital-output ratios in a country in which capital is the only scarce production factor therefore presupposes economic intercourse with countries of a different structure.

1.54 A phenomenon of considerable practical relevance is the diversity of the *periods of gestation* in different sectors, meaning that the investment process in one industry may take a much longer time than the investment process in another industry. In the models in this book, unlike current literature, more attention has been given to the consequences of the existence of different gestation lags.

1.55 In a considerable number of models, *prices* have been assumed to be constant and given; they can then conveniently be put equal to one, meaning that value figures and volume figures are identical. This is rather common practice in development programming. There are several reasons for it. As far as the general price level is concerned, it is not so very relevant to the physical side of long-term development. The nature of development was not so very different in times of a rising price level—say between 1850 and 1873 or between 1895 and 1913—and in times of a falling price level—say between 1873 and 1895. As long as such price rises or falls are slow, the economy can adapt itself to them relatively easily. Price rises of a catastrophic character are less easy to overcome, but they are unforeseeable anyhow. Relative price movements are more relevant to the structure of the economy, but for the majority of cases they are not outspoken and cannot be calculated easily. Even so, this side of the problem is sometimes relevant to development programming, especially when relative prices must be expected to move as a consequence of the expansion of certain lines of production. It seems useful, therefore, to formulate a bit more precisely the circumstances under which the *assumption of fixed prices* is appropriate.

In the first place, the assumption of fixed prices seems motivated when price levels are determined to a large extent by the world market and therefore cannot be influenced much by the program of the country considered. This will be so if (1) the country's supply of the relevant commodities is small in comparison with the world market and (2) free exchange possibilities exist. For commodities with high costs of transportation this will not apply; nor will it apply if there are serious restrictions to free transactions.

In the second place, a motivation for not assuming important relative price changes may be that it is the very objective of planning to maintain equilibrium between supply and demand and that in a way therefore price changes are assumed not to be necessary. Clearly this argument does not apply, however, when considerable economies of scale can be reaped as a consequence of the process of development.

Therefore, in some of our models, prices have been introduced explicitly as variables, in order to deal with cases in which clearly the program itself may be responsible for changes in relative prices.

1.56 A feature in need of some general comment is the phenomenon of *substitution*, so central in economic science. In some of the models, few possibilities of substitution have been explicitly or implicitly introduced. These models may well be somewhat rigid in comparison to reality; their value is sometimes of a didactic nature. As a rule, however, one or more forms of substitution have been assumed to exist. It seems useful to mention them in a systematic way.

One form of substitution is at the basis of the whole phenomenon of development and therefore is present everywhere in the book: the substitution possibility between present and future consumption, or *intertemporal substitution*. In models, however, in which the rate of saving is assumed given, this possibility has been disposed of.

The second type is substitution between factors of production. Substitution between labor and capital will be dealt with in Chap. 3, in a general way, and in Chap. 5 in more specific cases, which may arise in individual sectors (for example, factory versus cottage industry).

A third type of substitution is made possible by international trade. Since this aspect of planning has been neglected, considerable attention will be given to the methods applying to this type of substitution.

Finally, a fourth type of substitution occurs at the level of final consumption. Usually this form of substitution is induced by changes in relative prices. Prices as variables are introduced into the models in Chap. 6.

1.6. Arrangement of Subject Matter

1.61 Since this book deals with models rather than with specific policy problems, the subject matter has been arranged according to the type of models discussed. Various policy and planning problems can be treated with the same model and, inversely, a practical problem can be discussed with the aid of various models. By and large, the models have been arranged according to their degree of complexity: simpler models are discussed first, more difficult ones later. Planning agencies and students of planning not acquainted with the more complicated techniques may prefer to use only the simpler models. A larger role must be played then by trial-and-error and intuitive methods, which have to supplement the simpler models to a higher degree than the more complicated ones. Planning agencies equipped with a number of specialists may prefer to use the more complicated models.

The problems treated in this book must be seen mainly as examples illustrating the models. In actual programming, considerable attention must be given to the choice of aims and means of economic policy. For this subject the reader must be referred to other publications.[1] An example of the variety of problems which can be treated with the same model is given in Sec. 3.5.

1.62 The arrangement of the subject matter will be clear from the table of contents. Chapters 2 and 3 deal with what can be called macromodels, whereas the remaining chapters deal with micromodels in the sense that if one so wishes the number of sectors can be made large. Even so, some of the models in these chapters can also be kept small, that is, macromodels, the boundary being arbitrary. Chapters 2 and 4 deal with the more rigid models, within the categories just mentioned; 3 and 5 to 7 deal with the more flexible types, introducing one or more additional elements of choice by some form of substitution. Chapter 7 deals with sectors, a geographical subdivision into regions, and covers some new ground.

Chapter 8 finally formulates some critical remarks on models presented by others and adds some practical suggestions about the use to be made of the various categories of models.

[1] See Hollis B. Chenery, Development Policies and Programmes, *Econ. Bull. for Latin America,* vol. 3, p. 51, 1958; J. Tinbergen, "Economic Policy; Principles and Design," Amsterdam, 1956; "The Design of Development," Baltimore, 1958.

Chapter 2

ONE SCARCE FACTOR; ONE SECTOR

2.1. Macromodel; No Gestation Lag; No Depreciation

2.11 The models to be discussed in this chapter are the simplest models conceivable, thought to reflect the one phenomenon most characteristic of development, that is, the accumulation of capital. The one scarce factor considered is capital, and no other scarce factor is assumed to exist. Notwithstanding their extreme simplicity, these models can sometimes be used to make a first rough exploration of a country's growth process and to demonstrate some very fundamental relationships. These models or related ones have been introduced and discussed by R. F. Harrod and E. D. Domar.[1]

2.12 The variables used are

k capital stock[2]
y national income
j investment

The equations assumed are

$$\dot{k} = j \tag{2.12.1}$$

This equation states that, in the absence of a gestation lag and of depreciation, the rate of increase $\dot{k}$ ($= dk/dt$) of capital stock equals investment.

$$k = \kappa y \tag{2.12.2}$$

[1] R. F. Harrod, "Towards a Dynamic Economics," London, 1948; Evsey D. Domar, "Essays in the Theory of Economic Growth," New York, 1957.

[2] Since the role to be played by this variable depends on the production laws assumed, its definition will have to be adapted to these laws.

This equation expresses the assumption of a fixed *capital coefficient* (or *capital-output ratio*), representing a very simple production function.

$$j = \sigma y \tag{2.12.3}$$

This equation states that investment (assumed equal to savings) shows a fixed ratio σ to income; σ may be called the *savings ratio.*

2.13 The model admits a very simple solution of its system of equations, informing us about the speed of development.

$$\sigma y = j = \dot{k} = \kappa \dot{y} \tag{2.13.1}$$

or

$$\frac{\dot{y}}{y} = \frac{\sigma}{\kappa} \tag{2.13.2}$$

meaning that the rate of growth of income (and hence of both other variables) equals σ/κ.

As an example, let us take $\sigma = 0.12$ and $\kappa = 3$ years. Then evidently $\dot{y}/y = 0.04$ per annum; income, capital, and investment all grow 4 per cent per annum. Development over time of income can be represented by

$$y_t = y_0 e^{\sigma t/\kappa} \tag{2.13.3}$$

where y_0 is income at time $t = 0$. This income, or, alternatively, the initial value of capital (k_0) or investments (j_0), has to be given in order that the development path may be determined.

The formulas may be interpreted as the solution of an analytical problem in which σ and κ are given and the rate of development follows. Inversely, a political problem may be solved with them by considering the *desired rate of growth* of income ω given and calculating the *required rate of savings* σ'.

$$\sigma' = \omega\kappa \tag{2.13.4}$$

2.14 The model may be supplemented with more variables and equations which do not change the relationships already discussed. This will always be the case if the new variables are dependent on the variables already discussed without changing the equations already discussed. The simplest example is the addition of the variable c, standing for consumption and satisfying the relation $c = y - j$.

Other variables may be added for an *open* country, namely, imports i and exports e, as well as gross product v.* The relations to be added may be

$$i = \iota v \tag{2.14.1}$$

$$v = y + i = c + j + e \tag{2.14.2}$$

$$e = i \tag{2.14.3}$$

* The use of the word "gross" here means that product is taken at the *final* stage, that is, when reaching the consumer, the investor, or the country to which exported. For a nation as a whole v is also called *total resources.*

The latter equation is a consequence of our assumption $c = y - j$ and expresses the well-known equivalence between internal financial equilibrium and balance-of-payments equilibrium. It should be noted, however, that there is an implicit assumption in these equations, namely, that exports to the volume of e are salable at the (constant) price level assumed.

2.2. Macromodel; No Gestation Lag; with Depreciation and Replacement

2.21 The models to be treated in this section are characterized by the assumption of a finite lifetime Θ of all capital goods. This assumption makes it desirable to distinguish between the stock b of equipment or capital goods and the stock k of capital. The difference between the two concepts is to be found in the fact that an individual machine remains a constant volume of equipment until it is scrapped, whereas its contribution to the capital stock falls because of its depreciation. Our assumption implies that no obsolescence occurs; otherwise the contribution to b may not be constant. In order not to complicate the model unnecessarily, linear depreciation will be assumed. The model brings out some interesting features of development under these assumptions.

2.22 The variables used are

b volume of equipment
k volume of capital
v gross product
d depreciation allowances
r replacement
c consumption
s savings
j^G gross investment
j net investment
y net product

The equations of the model are, with their motivations,

$$\dot{b} = j^G - r \tag{2.22.1}$$

The net addition to the stock of equipment can be found by deducting replacement from gross investment.

$$\dot{k} = s \tag{2.22.2}$$

The net additions to capital are equal to savings.

$$b = \kappa' v \tag{2.22.3}$$

Gross product is taken to be proportional to the volume (or *capacity*) of equipment, κ' representing a *gross capital coefficient.*

$$j = j^G - d \tag{2.22.4}$$

Net investment equals gross investment minus depreciation.

$$r_t = j^G_{t-\Theta} \tag{2.22.5}$$

Replacement equals gross investment one lifetime before.

$$d = \frac{b}{\Theta} \tag{2.22.6}$$

Depreciation allowances are equal to the new value of total equipment divided by lifetime. The essence of what is here called new value is that it is value without deduction of depreciation.

$$y = v - d \tag{2.22.7}$$

Income equals gross product minus depreciation. Since no imports are assumed to exist in this version of the model, no deduction of imports is necessary.

$$y = c + s \tag{2.22.8}$$

From the spending side, income equals consumption plus savings. No lags are assumed to occur in this relationship.

$$s = j \tag{2.22.9}$$

Savings are equal to net investment.

$$s = \sigma y \tag{2.22.10}$$

Savings are a portion σ of income, where σ is the savings rate.

2.23 Also, this system of relations admits a relatively simple solution, although less simple than the previous model. Since the system is linear, the usual method will do, which consists in assuming a solution of the shape[1]

$$j^G = j_0{}^G e^{\omega t} \tag{2.23.1}$$

where $j_0{}^G$ is an arbitrary constant representing the initial value of j^G and ω a constant which will have to satisfy some condition to be found from the system of equations.

It can be easily found that

$$r_t = j^G_{t-\Theta} = j_0{}^G e^{\omega(t-\Theta)} \tag{2.23.2}$$
$$\dot{b} = j^G - r = j_0{}^G e^{\omega t}(1 - e^{-\omega\Theta}) \tag{2.23.3}$$

[1] See, e.g., Lyman M. Kells, "Elementary Differential Equations," p. 87, New York and London, 1935.

from which it follows that[1]

$$b = \frac{1}{\omega} j_0{}^G e^{\omega t}(1 - e^{-\omega\Theta}) \tag{2.23.4}$$

From b we can derive v and d:

$$v = \frac{b}{\kappa'} \qquad \text{and} \qquad d = \frac{b}{\Theta}$$

leading to

$$j^G - d = j = s = \sigma y = \sigma(v - d) = \sigma\left(\frac{1}{\kappa'} - \frac{1}{\Theta}\right) b \tag{2.23.5}$$

Upon filling out the expressions for j^G, d, and b, we find the condition

$$\omega = \left(\frac{\sigma}{\kappa'} + \frac{1 - \sigma}{\Theta}\right)(1 - e^{-\omega\Theta}) \tag{2.23.6}$$

A complete solution for j^G and the other variables consists of as many terms of the shape shown in (2.23.1) as there are roots of Eq. (2.23.6).

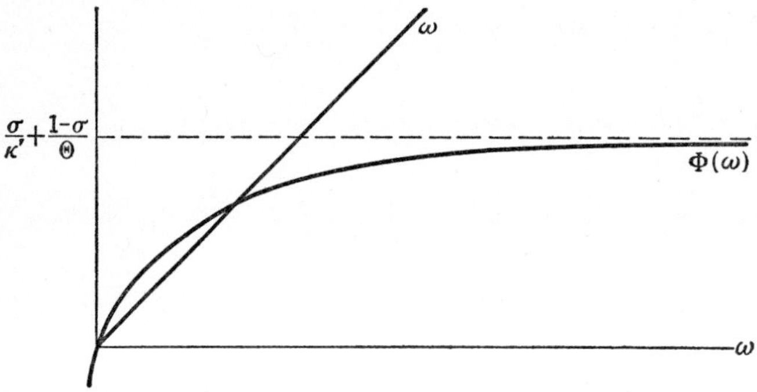

Fig. 1

Roots may be real or complex; complex roots correspond to fluctuating movements of the variables. The nature of real roots—to which, as long as $\omega > 0$, monotonically rising movements of the variables correspond—can be illustrated by Fig. 1. Let the right-hand side of (2.23.6) be represented by

$$\Phi(\omega) = \left(\frac{\sigma}{\kappa'} + \frac{1 - \sigma}{\Theta}\right)(1 - e^{-\omega\Theta})$$

Then the root ω_0 will be represented by the point of intersection between the straight line with slope 1 (of which the ordinates are ω) and the curve with ordinates $\Phi(\omega)$. It can be shown that for $\sigma > 0$ and $\Theta > \kappa'$, both

[1] No additive constant can be added to (2.23.4), since then the relation (2.22.5) would be violated.

realistic assumptions, there is always such an intersection point. An explicit solution is not possible, but for small values of $\omega\Theta$ the expression $e^{-\omega\Theta}$ can be approximated by $1 - \omega\Theta + \frac{1}{2}\omega^2\Theta^2 \cdots$ leading to

$$\omega = \left(\frac{\sigma}{\kappa'} + \frac{1-\sigma}{\Theta}\right)\left(\omega\Theta - \frac{1}{2}\,\omega^2\Theta^2\right)$$

or

$$\omega = 2\sigma\left(\frac{1}{\kappa'} - \frac{1}{\Theta}\right)$$

For large values of Θ, on the other hand, the Domar-Harrod result $\omega = \sigma/\kappa'$ will be obtained, as can be seen directly from (2.23.6). Evidently, there are no other real roots.

2.24 The solutions can be used for the *analytical problem* to explain development with given values of the coefficients, including the savings ratio σ, and with given initial values of the variables, such as $j_0{}^G$, etc. In such a problem also the complex roots of (2.23.6) will have to play their part. Only when a sufficient number of terms of the general form (2.23.1) [where, however, the constant factors are not now identical to $j_0{}^G$, since that only applies if only one term is taken, as in (2.23.1)] is introduced is it possible to solve the analytical problem with given initial values of the variables. These initial values may, however, be such as to let the system move along cycles.

For the solution of the *political problem*, the situation is different. There is scope here to consider as the aim a pattern of *development without cyclical setbacks*. In our mathematical language, this means that only one root, namely the real one, of Eq. (2.23.6) is relevant to us and accordingly Eqs. (2.23.1) to (2.23.5) are valid, with $j_0{}^G$ equal to the initial value of j^G, whereas all other initial values can be calculated from it. This means that, in order to warrant a noncyclical movement, certain relationships between the initial variables must be satisfied. If, in addition, a certain rate of development ω_0 is desired, the rate of savings σ_0 can be derived from (2.23.6); it should be

$$\sigma_0 = \frac{\omega_0/(1 - e^{-\omega_0\Theta}) - 1/\Theta}{1/\kappa' - 1/\Theta} \tag{2.24.1}$$

It will again easily be seen that for $\Theta = \infty$ this expression coincides with (2.13.4).

2.25 Once a development pattern of this kind is followed, there will exist fixed ratios between the variables. This is a consequence, of course, of a number of simplifying assumptions implied in our model. Later we shall discuss models where this somewhat unrealistic feature has been removed. It seems interesting, however, to calculate some of the ratios that may make sense, if only approximately, under more general conditions. We shall calculate k/y, k/b, and r/d.

Starting from (2.23.5) we have

$$\dot{k} = s = \sigma\left(\frac{1}{\kappa'} - \frac{1}{\Theta}\right)b \tag{2.25.1}$$

Using (2.23.4) we find

$$\dot{k} = \frac{\sigma}{\omega}\left(\frac{1}{\kappa'} - \frac{1}{\Theta}\right)j_0{}^G e^{\omega t}(1 - e^{-\omega\Theta}) \tag{2.25.2}$$

By integration over time and by requiring that k should approach zero for $t = -\infty$, where the other variables so far considered also vanish, we have

$$k = \frac{\sigma}{\omega^2}\left(\frac{1}{\kappa'} - \frac{1}{\Theta}\right)j_0{}^G e^{\omega t}(1 - e^{-\omega\Theta}) \tag{2.25.3}$$

We can now calculate the three ratios mentioned:

$$\frac{k}{y} = \frac{\sigma}{\omega} \qquad \frac{k}{b} = \frac{\sigma}{\omega}\left(\frac{1}{\kappa'} - \frac{1}{\Theta}\right) \qquad \frac{r}{d} = \frac{\omega\Theta}{e^{\omega\Theta} - 1} \tag{2.25.4}$$

For the political problem it is desirable to express them in terms of ω, as can be done explicitly with the aid of (2.23.6); the results are

$$\frac{k}{y} = \frac{1/(1 - e^{-\omega\Theta}) - 1/\omega\Theta}{1/\kappa' - 1/\Theta} \qquad \frac{k}{b} = \frac{1}{1 - e^{-\omega\Theta}} - \frac{1}{\omega\Theta} \qquad \frac{r}{d} = \frac{\omega\Theta}{e^{\omega\Theta} - 1} \tag{2.25.5}$$

For very small and very large values of $\omega\Theta$ these expressions can be further simplified. The results are shown below.

	k/y	k/b	r/d
$\omega\Theta$ small	$\dfrac{\frac{1}{2}}{1/\kappa' - 1/\Theta}$	$\frac{1}{2}$	1
$\omega\Theta$ large	κ'	1	0

2.26 The model remains simpler if instead of Eq. (2.22.3), representing a purely technological production function, the more customary but less clear relationship

$$k = \kappa y \tag{2.26.1}$$

is maintained. In this case, as in Sec. 2.14, k, s, or j and y remain an inner circle of variables, the movements of which are independent from the equations outside (2.22.2), (2.22.10), and (2.26.1). We have

$$\dot{k} = \frac{\sigma}{\kappa}k \tag{2.26.2}$$

and hence $k = k_0 e^{\omega t}$ satisfies, with

$$\omega = \frac{\sigma}{\kappa} \tag{2.26.3}$$

As a consequence $y = (k_0/\kappa)e^{\sigma t/\kappa}$.

The remaining variables may be determined by first considering b, which has to satisfy

$$\dot{b} = j^G - j^G_{t-\Theta} = \sigma y + \frac{b}{\Theta} - \sigma y_{t-\Theta} - \frac{b_{t-\Theta}}{\Theta} \tag{2.26.4}$$

This is a linear nonhomogeneous difference-differential equation. The general solution consists of two parts: (1) the general solution of the homogeneous equation

$$\Theta \dot{b}_t = b_t - b_{t-\Theta} \tag{2.26.5}$$

and (2) a particular solution of the nonhomogeneous equation.[1] It is easily seen that the general solution of (2.26.5) runs

$$b_t = b^{00} + b^{01}t \tag{2.26.6}$$

If, however, we require that for $t = -\infty$, b_t should be zero, it will appear that this solution is discarded again.

A particular solution of the nonhomogeneous equation may be attempted by assuming $b_t = b_0 e^{\omega t}$ where $\omega = \sigma/\kappa$, as in (2.26.3). This solution is admissible only when b_0 satisfies

$$\omega = (1 - e^{-\omega\Theta})\left(\frac{\sigma}{\kappa}\frac{k_0}{b_0} + \frac{1}{\Theta}\right) \tag{2.26.7}$$

Since σ has to be adapted, in the political problem, to the desired rate of growth ω, this expression can then be transformed into

$$\frac{k_0}{b_0} = \frac{1}{1 - e^{-\omega\Theta}} - \frac{1}{\omega\Theta} \tag{2.26.8}$$

It is interesting to note that this formula is identical with the one shown for k/b in (2.25.5).

The remaining variables can be derived from the equations connecting them with the variables already determined.

2.3. Macromodel with Gestation Lag; No Depreciation

2.31 A somewhat unrealistic feature of the models so far discussed is the absence of a gestation lag. Each unit of investment, however small, is supposed immediately to add to the capital stock. It will now be assumed that a time lag θ occurs between the start of any investment process (say building) and the addition to the capital stock of a finished

[1] See, e.g., Kells, *op. cit.*, p. 93.

capital good. The introduction of this phenomenon necessitates the addition of assumptions about the investment process during this time period. We shall first make the simplest conceivable hypothesis, namely, that the process requires a uniform input of effort during the period θ.

It is useful to introduce as a new variable "investment finished," to be indicated by j'_t. By definition we shall then have

$$\dot{k}_t = j'_t \tag{2.31.1}$$

Total investment activity j_t at any time period t is now the total of activities started and not yet finished, that is, activities of which the time of finishing is between t and $t + \theta$. Since all are running at an even pace, activity j is only an unweighted average:

$$j_t = \frac{1}{\theta} \int_t^{t+\theta} j' \, dt' \tag{2.31.2}$$

This expression can be transformed with the aid of (2.31.1):

$$j_t = \frac{1}{\theta} k_{t'} \Big|_t^{t+\theta} = \frac{1}{\theta} (k_{t+\theta} - k_t) \tag{2.31.2'}$$

Adding Eqs. (2.12.3) and (2.12.2), we have a system of four equations for our four variables.

2.32 The solution of the system can be found by expressing j_t in terms of k_t with the aid of the last two equations, yielding

$$j_t = \frac{\sigma}{\kappa} k_t = \frac{1}{\theta} (k_{t+\theta} - k_t) \tag{2.32.1}$$

which may be rewritten

$$k_{t+\theta} = \left(1 + \frac{\theta\sigma}{\kappa}\right) k_t \tag{2.32.2}$$

The same equation will also hold for the other variables. During a period θ, capital will have grown in the ratio $1 + \theta\sigma/\kappa$. Disregarding fluctuations with a period smaller than θ, we may write the solution

$$k_t = k_0 \left(1 + \frac{\theta\sigma}{\kappa}\right)^{t/\theta} \tag{2.32.3}$$

from which we can derive

$$\frac{\dot{k}_t}{k_t} = \frac{1}{\theta} \ln \left(1 + \frac{\theta\sigma}{\kappa}\right) \tag{2.32.4}$$

It is easily seen that for small values of $\theta\sigma/\kappa$ this becomes identical to σ/κ, that is, the rate of growth found in Eq. (2.13.2) holding for the model without gestation lag. For larger values of $\theta\sigma/\kappa$, the deviations from the rate previously found may be considerable; growth will be slower.

2.33 The investment process may be of a different kind. Another simple example is that of a point input at the beginning of the lag, followed by the same point output we assumed in the previous case. Here we simply have

$$j_t = j'_{t+\theta} \tag{2.33.1}$$

Consequently we find

$$\dot{k}_t = j'_t = j_{t-\theta} = \frac{\sigma}{\kappa} k_{t-\theta} \tag{2.33.2}$$

Again writing $k_t = k_0 e^{\omega t}$, we find that ω will have to satisfy

$$\omega = \frac{\sigma}{\kappa} e^{-\omega\theta} \tag{2.33.3}$$

Again, for small values of $\omega\theta$ we find $\omega = \sigma/\kappa$.

2.4. The Optimum Rate of Development[1]

2.41 A practical problem of considerable importance consists in deciding upon the rate of growth of production to be chosen. The well-known fact that in communist countries these rates and, as a consequence, the rates of saving applied are almost double those of noncommunist countries[2] illustrates the wide differences in decisions taken. The question may therefore be asked whether economic science can give a clue to a numerical choice.

Attempts made by the present authors seem to justify a negative answer. Nevertheless, it seems worth while to describe the attempts and their results. An attempt was made so to interpret the problem that the optimum rate of development was the one maximizing utility over time and to utilize the scarce efforts made at measuring the relevant properties of the utility function. Maximization of utility as a device is in any case superior to maximization of consumption, which again is better than maximization of income. The specific interpretation given to utility was the assumption that it depends only on consumption in the same time unit; this may be too restrictive, as will be discussed later, but no measurements at all are available for the dependence of utility of consumption at other time periods.

2.42 Various types of *utility functions* were assumed; it appeared desirable to introduce a minimum level $\bar{c}$ of consumption, below which

[1] This section may be skipped by the reader interested only in practical planning.

[2] In the United States the average savings ratio over a business cycle has long been 11 to 12 per cent; for the United Kingdom a slightly higher figure has been found. At present, savings ratios in Western Europe are higher. Savings ratios in communist countries cannot be compared easily, for several reasons, but figures of 25 per cent in terms of Western concepts have been mentioned.

marginal utility becomes infinitely large. Further exploration taught the authors that it is also desirable to introduce a maximum or saturation level c^m above $\bar{c}$, that is, $c = c^m + \bar{c}$, at which the marginal utility is zero. The utility function to be used in this section will be written

$$u = \left(\frac{c^m}{c - \bar{c}} - 1\right)^v \qquad (2.42.1)$$

where u is marginal utility and v a constant. Its value was derived from Frisch's well-known estimates[1] of the flexibility of marginal utility, originally based on the assumption that sugar is an "independent" commodity, an assumption later removed, however, to some extent. In order to arrive at one single value for v, it was necessary to complete Frisch's estimates by a few more assumptions. Frisch estimated the flexibility of marginal utility for two groups of workers, an American group, for which he found -1, and a French group, for which he found -3.5. Our assumptions are that (1) the same utility function holds for both and that (2) the level of consumption of French workers, at the time of measurement, was one-half the level of American workers.

Flexibility being defined as $(\partial u/\partial c)\, c/u$, it appears to be

$$-\frac{vc^m}{(c - \bar{c})^2}\left(\frac{c^m}{c - \bar{c}} - 1\right)^{v-1} \frac{c}{[c^m/(c - \bar{c}) - 1]^v} = -\frac{vc^m c}{c^m + \bar{c} - c}\,\frac{1}{c - \bar{c}} \qquad (2.42.2)$$

Indicating French consumption by c^F and hence American consumption by $2c^F$, we have, according to Frisch,

$$\frac{2c^m vc^F}{(c^m + \bar{c} - 2c^F)(2c^F - \bar{c})} = 1 \quad \text{and} \quad \frac{c^m vc^F}{(c^m + \bar{c} - c^F)(c^F - \bar{c})} = 3.5 \qquad (2.42.3)$$

Adding the further assumption that c^m is large in comparison with $2c^F$, we have, approximately,

$$\frac{2vc^F}{2c^F - \bar{c}} = 1 \qquad \frac{vc^F}{c^F - \bar{c}} = 3.5 \qquad (2.42.4)$$

From these equations we find that $v = 0.6$ and $\bar{c}/c^F = 5/6$. This second result does not seem to be unrealistic, and may justify some confidence in the result for v too.

No *discount* for future consumption was applied in the belief that for a country's planning, future generations should count as much as present generations. According to this philosophy, a discount may be realistic for the individual's plans but not necessarily for a nation's. It is not difficult to introduce discounts for future consumption when so desired,

[1] Ragnar Frisch, "New Methods of Measuring Marginal Utility," Tübingen, 1932.

but the question then arises at what level the discount should be put. Instead of a discount, a finite horizon T may be introduced; a similar question then comes up about its length.

Population was assumed to remain constant. It is not difficult, however, to assume a certain rate of growth π and change the formulas accordingly. In a general way this will raise the optimum rate of savings in the well-known way, that is, by $\pi\kappa$, when a fixed capital-output ratio is assumed.

This, in fact, was the *production function* utilized. As long as capital is the scarcest factor, this assumption may be a proper approximation. It appeared to be very difficult, if not impossible, to find an explicit solution if a more complicated production function were assumed to exist, for example, the Cobb-Douglas function.

2.43 The *problem of the optimum rate of development* was then given the following formal shape. Given an initial income y_0 and a capital-output ratio κ (implying, if one likes, an initial capital stock $k_0 = \kappa y_0$) and given the utility function (2.42.1), what program $c(t)$ of consumption (implying a program of saving and hence of capital expansion) yields maximum satisfaction over time $\int_0^\infty U(t')\,dt'$, where U is total utility of consumption at time t'?

Evidently the maximum is one with a *side condition*, namely, that at any time t (using symbols as before), $c + s = y$ or, with $s = j = \dot{k} = \kappa\dot{y}$

$$c + \kappa\dot{y} = y \tag{2.43.1}$$

Apart from this side condition, we shall also consider two *boundary conditions*, namely,

$$c \geq \bar{c} \qquad s \geq 0 \tag{2.43.2}$$

As long as these boundary conditions are not active, that is, income is actually distributed between some positive savings and a volume of consumption surpassing the subsistence minimum $\bar{c}$, for all time units considered, that is, for $0 \leq t \leq \infty$, the maximum requires that the marginal utility of consumption at moment t equals the total marginal utility of the additional consumption in the future to be obtained from giving up one unit of consumption at time t. Since the increase in future production made possible by giving up one unit of consumption is $1/\kappa$ for all the future, the condition runs

$$u_t = \frac{1}{\kappa}\int_t^\infty u_t\,dt' \tag{2.43.3}$$

It does not matter that this future production may not actually be consumed but partly saved; this decision can be separated from the one at time t. If this future decision again obeys (2.43.3), the marginal utility of the corresponding addition to production can be measured either on the consumption or on the savings side; these two are equal.

Equation (2.43.3) may be replaced by one which is simpler to handle, by replacing both sides by their derivatives with regard to time. We must later test, however, whether (2.43.3) is then also satisfied, depending on the integration constant applied. The new equation runs

$$\frac{du}{dt} = -\frac{u}{\kappa} \tag{2.43.4}$$

Since u depends on t via c, it is better to rewrite it

$$\kappa \frac{du}{dc} \dot{c} = -u$$

Using (2.42.1), we obtain

$$\dot{c}' = \frac{c^m - c'}{\kappa v c^m} c' \tag{2.43.5}$$

where $c' = c - \bar{c}$. Since this equation only contains the variable c' and not the other variable y of our system, its integration can be undertaken separately. Equation (2.43.5) is the well-known differential equation of the logistic curve; the integral may be written

$$c' = \frac{c^m}{1 + Be^{-t/\kappa v}} \tag{2.43.6}$$

where $B = e^{t_0/\kappa v}$ is an arbitrary constant which may be replaced by t_0, the time at which $c' = \frac{1}{2}c^m$, that is, half the level of the asymptote.

Our result means that consumption will gradually have to approach, but never have to reach, the saturation level $c^m + \bar{c}$.

2.44 The next step consists in integrating Eq. (2.43.1) for y, which can now be written

$$y' - \kappa \dot{y}' = \frac{c^m}{1 + Be^{-t/\kappa v}} \tag{2.44.1}$$

when

$$y' = y - \bar{c} \tag{2.44.2}$$

and evidently represents a nonhomogeneous first-order linear differential equation. A standard method to deal with the left-hand side of the equation is to calculate the derivative of $y'e^{-t/\kappa}$ with respect to time:

$$\frac{d}{dt} y'e^{-t/\kappa} = e^{-t/\kappa}\left(\dot{y}' - \frac{y'}{\kappa}\right)$$

According to (2.44.1), this expression must be equal to

$$-\frac{c^m e^{-t/\kappa}}{\kappa(1 + Be^{-t/\kappa v})}$$

Hence we have

$$y'e^{-t/\kappa} = -\frac{c^m}{\kappa}\int \frac{e^{-t'/\kappa}\,dt'}{1 + Be^{-t'/\kappa\upsilon}} \tag{2.44.3}$$

It appears possible to carry out explicitly this integration for integer values of $1/\upsilon$. Since our estimate $\upsilon = 0.6$ is a rough approximation, it seems worth while carrying out the integration for $\upsilon = 0.5$ or $1/\upsilon = 2$. This can be done with the aid of the substitution

$$Be^{-2t'/\kappa} = t''^2$$

where t'' is a new integration variable. It follows that $e^{-t'/\kappa}\sqrt{B} = t''$

and
$$-\frac{\sqrt{B}}{\kappa}e^{-t'/\kappa}\,dt' = dt''$$

The integral (2.44.3) now becomes

$$\frac{\kappa}{c^m}y'e^{-t/\kappa} = \frac{\kappa}{\sqrt{B}}\int \frac{dt''}{1 + t''^2} \tag{2.44.4}$$

or
$$y' = \frac{c^m}{\sqrt{B}}e^{t/\kappa}\arctan t'' + \bar{y} = \frac{c^m}{\sqrt{B}}e^{t/\kappa}\arctan e^{-t/\kappa}\sqrt{B} + \bar{y}$$

where $\bar{y}$ is an arbitrary constant the value of which has to be determined with the aid of boundary conditions.

A natural boundary condition, to be added to the initial condition that y_0 be given, is that for $t = \infty$, y approaches c; in fact, there is no reason to save at the saturation level, because there is no reason to surpass that level. Economic development finds its natural end when saturation is approached. Since for $t = \infty$

$$\frac{\arctan e^{-t/\kappa}\sqrt{B}}{e^{-t/\kappa}\sqrt{B}} = 1$$

$y' = c^m + \bar{y}$ and hence $\bar{y} = 0$.

The solution for y therefore is

$$y_t = \frac{c^m}{e^{-t/\kappa}\sqrt{B}}\arctan e^{-t/\kappa}\sqrt{B} + \bar{c} \tag{2.44.5}$$

This implies that

$$y_0 = c^m\frac{\arctan\sqrt{B}}{\sqrt{B}} + \bar{c} \tag{2.44.6}$$

Production and hence capital must develop, according to (2.44.5), along a curve very similar to a logistic; both curves are characterized by a moderate slope in the early phases, increasing in acceleration until a certain point and then slowing down again and approximating a horizontal asymptote.

2.45 The nature of the movements found may be illustrated by substituting for the last section an alternative setup which seems more illuminating from the mathematical point of view and not even a bad approximation from a practical economic point of view. Writing instead of $\dot{y}$ in Eq. (2.43.1) $(y_t - y_{t-\kappa})/\kappa$, that is, the average rate of

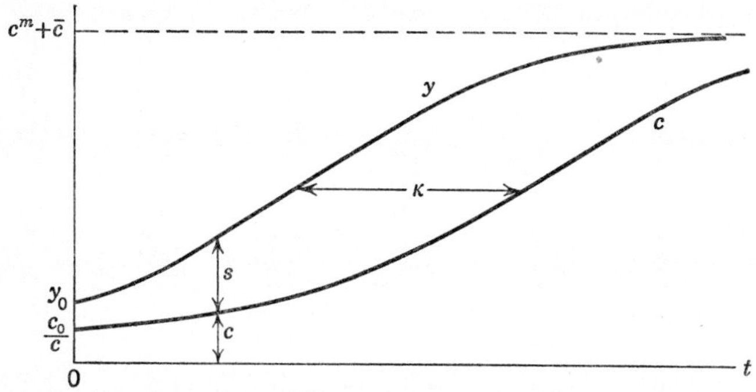

Fig. 2

increase over the last κ time units (practically some three to four years), we find that this equation takes a particularly simple shape

$$c_t + y_t - y_{t-\kappa} = y_t \tag{2.45.1}$$

leading immediately to the solution

$$y_{t-\kappa} = c_t$$

or

$$y_t = c_{t+\kappa} \tag{2.45.2}$$

The practical justification for this alternative setup may be that investments are based on the rate of increase in income experienced in the last three to four years, rather than the last small time unit, indeed appealing to the economist. The nature of the result then becomes very simple: both consumption and production have to move along a logistic, the only difference between the two being a time lag of κ time units (cf. Fig. 2). The logistic for y has to be located so as to leave an intercept on the vertical axis of y_0.

Savings are measured by the vertical distance between the two curves. In the beginning they are small; they may become quite substantial, absolutely as well as relatively speaking, but in the end, when half the saturation level of consumption has been passed, they diminish and finally peter out.

2.46 We may finish this exercise by making an attempt at measuring the rates of saving following from our formulas under various circumstances. As a consequence of our first boundary condition (2.43.2), no savings are envisaged whenever $y_0 = \bar{c}$. As a consequence, no development will take place either, and consumption and production will remain on the subsistence level. Initial savings will have to be positive, however, whenever $y_0 > \bar{c}$; in the beginning they may be small, but they will increase, and during the full swing of the development process, they will have to be considerable. This may be shown by calculating the maximum rate of savings following from the formulas. Writing again

$$t'' = e^{-t/\kappa}\sqrt{B} \tag{2.46.1}$$

we have

$$c = \frac{c^m}{1 + t''^2} + \bar{c} \tag{2.46.2}$$

and

$$y = \frac{c^m \arctan t''}{t''} + \bar{c} \tag{2.46.3}$$

from which we derive, for the savings rate σ,

$$\sigma = 1 - \frac{c}{y} = 1 - \frac{c^m/(1 + t''^2) + \bar{c}}{(c^m/t'') \arctan t'' + \bar{c}} \tag{2.46.4}$$

It is more elegant now to introduce $t''' = \arctan t''$, or $t'' = \tan t'''$; writing also A for $c^m/\bar{c}$, we find

$$\sigma = \frac{1 - (\sin 2t''')/2t'''}{1 + \dfrac{1}{A}\dfrac{\tan t'''}{t'''}} \tag{2.46.5}$$

Since

$$y = \bar{c}\left(A\frac{t'''}{\tan t'''} + 1\right)$$

and $t'''/\tan t'''$ is a decreasing function of t''', t''' evidently has its highest value for the initial value y_0 of y and then decreases.

As can be seen from (2.46.5), the maximum value of σ depends only on A, at least as long as y_0 is below the value of y corresponding with that maximum σ. For y_0 low, in comparison with $c^m + \bar{c}$, this always applies. Computation shows that σ_{max} is quite high, as is illustrated by the following figures:

A	σ_{max}
10	0.63
100	0.86
500	0.94

2.47 From the values shown it appears that the model used leads to unrealistically high values for the optimum rate of savings. In fact, the formulas have the tendency to recommend austerity in order to reach the saturation level "as soon as possible." This may be illustrated by calculating the rate of increase in consumption for the level $\frac{1}{2}c^m + \bar{c}$, that is, halfway between the subsistence level and the saturation level and asking ourselves how much time it would take, at this rate of increase, to reach the saturation level. From formula (2.43.5) it follows that $\dot{c} = \dot{c}' = c^m/2$ for $c' = \frac{1}{2}c^m$, meaning that, at that speed, the distance from $\bar{c}$ to $c^m + \bar{c}$ takes 2κ years or 6 to 8 years only. Even though the actual time will be longer, since the speed at halfway is the maximum, it illustrates the order of magnitude involved.

There seem to be two main reasons why actual savings rates are so much lower. On the one hand, individuals do discount future consumption, although we disregarded this phenomenon. On the other hand, savings programs near the ones implied in our formulas always mean that the present generation is suffering for the coming generations to an extent that is not generally considered proper. If, therefore, the element of "more justice in the relations between generations" were brought into our utility concept, we would obtain lower savings as the optimum program. Since no attempts to measure the preference schedules implied are known to us, we have not tried to generalize our findings along these lines. Our conclusion with regard to the question whether economic science can indicate an optimum rate of development tends to be negative therefore.

Chapter 3

SEVERAL SCARCE FACTORS; ONE SECTOR

3.1. Population-Capital-Technical–Change Model; Continuous Substitution between Factors

3.11 We shall now consider models with more than one scarce factor of production. In order to show the consequences of this generalization in the simplest possible way, we shall stick to the assumption of only one sector, that is, one product. Our models will have only two scarce factors, to be called capital and labor. They can also be land and labor, or any other pair. It is possible to generalize the results in order to apply them to the cases of a larger number of factors.

To begin with, it will be assumed that the two factors are perfectly substitutable. More restricted possibilities of substitution will be considered later (see Sec. 3.4). Since the simplest example of perfect substitution between two factors is represented by the well-known Cobb-Douglas production function, and since observation does not contradict the main implications of this function, we shall use this function throughout this section and the next few. The function will be given the so-called generalized shape

$$v = (1 + \epsilon)^t a^\lambda k^\mu \tag{3.11.1}$$

where v is production volume

a is quantity of labor employed, or employment

k is quantity of capital used

ϵ is the annual rise in efficiency[1]

λ and μ are the elasticities of production with regard to labor and capital, respectively

t is time

[1] As will be clear from the formula, ϵ indicates the annual rise in production with the aid of constant quantities of labor and capital, and hence implies the consequences of changes in working hours.

We shall develop most of our formulas, however, on the specific assumption that $\lambda + \mu = 1$, meaning that there are, for the country considered, no economies of scale. This assumption could be justified by pointing to the fact that for the majority of industries the optimum size of the enterprise is small in comparison with the total market. As a consequence, expansion of production will, as a rule, have to be obtained by increasing the number of enterprises of optimum size, implying constant returns or no economies of scale.

3.12 The variables of the model are, including those already mentioned,

- v volume of production
- a quantity of labor employed or employment
- k quantity of capital used
- k^0 quantity of capital in existence
- P size of population
- l real wage rate
- m real income per unit of capital
- l^0 real wage rate considered normal or appropriate

This last variable enters into the labor supply function (see Sec. 3.13) as a psychological reference variable indicative of the gradual development in the ideas of the population—probably based on past experience—as to what is a normal, an appropriate, or a reasonable wage level.

3.13 The following relations constitute the model. The *production function* already mentioned represents the collection of technological possibilities:

$$v = (1 + \epsilon)^t a^\lambda k^{1-\lambda} \tag{3.13.1}$$

The meaning of the constants ϵ and λ has already been discussed in Sec. 3.11.

Since perfect competition between employers will be assumed, *demand for labor* and *for capital* will be such as to equate their price to their marginal productivities. Hence

$$l = \frac{\partial v}{\partial a} = \lambda(1 + \epsilon)^t \left(\frac{k}{a}\right)^{1-\lambda} \tag{3.13.2}$$

$$m = \frac{\partial v}{\partial k} = (1 - \lambda)(1 + \epsilon)^t \left(\frac{a}{k}\right)^{\lambda} \tag{3.13.3}$$

The *supply of labor* connects the proportion a/P of the population willing to work with the ratio l/l_0 of the wage rate to the "normal" wage rate.

$$\frac{l}{l^0} = \left(\frac{a}{P}\right)^\alpha \tag{3.13.4}$$

where α is the flexibility of supply ($1/\alpha$ is the elasticity of supply).

The *background variables* l^0 and P appearing in this equation are supposed to move in an autonomous way.

$$l^0 = l_0^0(1 + \Omega)^t \tag{3.13.5}$$
$$P = P_0(1 + \pi)^t \tag{3.13.6}$$

where l_0^0 and P_0 are the values at $t = 0$ of l^0 and P, respectively, and Ω and π are the annual rates of increase of the normal wage rate and population, successively.

Equations (3.13.4) to (3.13.6) may be combined to

$$l = \left[\frac{a}{P_0(1 + \pi)^t}\right]^\alpha l_0^0(1 + \Omega)^t \tag{3.13.4$'$}$$

The *supply of capital* k depends on the total quantity in existence, k^0, and the rate of interest m both having a positive influence on k. We shall write the supply function in the following form:

$$m = \left(\frac{k}{k^0}\right)^\beta \tag{3.13.7}$$

Here β is the supply flexibility. It would have been possible to introduce a "normal interest rate" m^0, as in the case of the supply of labor, but we shall not go into this in much detail here, since, as a rule, the supply of capital is assumed to be inelastic, meaning that $k = k^0$, irrespective of the value of m^0 and m.

The *formation of capital*, finally, is assumed to be linked with national product or income by the simple equation

$$\dot{k}^0 = \sigma v \tag{3.13.8}$$

where σ represents the propensity to save, supposed constant. Because of the special shape of the production function, the shares of income going to capital and labor are constant. Even when savings are assumed to be made by capital owners only, there is no objection to the assumption of a constant value of σ.

Equations (3.13.1) to (3.13.3), (3.13.4′), (3.13.7), and (3.13.8) enable us to calculate the development over time of the six variables a, k^0, k, v, l, and m.

3.14 As an example, we shall explicitly determine the time shape of development for the simplest case where the *supply elasticity both of labor and of capital are zero*, or α and β infinite. In fact these assumptions simplify Eqs. (3.13.4′) and (3.13.7); they become

$$a = P_0(1 + \pi)^t \tag{3.14.1}$$
$$k = k^0 \tag{3.14.2}$$

Combining them with (3.13.1) and (3.13.8), we have

$$\dot{k} = \sigma v = \sigma(1+\epsilon)^t P_0^\lambda (1+\pi)^{\lambda t} k^{1-\lambda}$$

or

$$\dot{k}k^{\lambda-1} = \sigma P_0^\lambda [(1+\epsilon)(1+\pi)^\lambda]^t \tag{3.14.3}$$

Since $(d/dt)k^\lambda = \lambda k^{\lambda-1}\dot{k}$, we have

$$\frac{d}{dt} k^\lambda = \lambda\sigma P_0^\lambda [(1+\epsilon)(1+\pi)^\lambda]^t = \lambda\sigma P_0^\lambda e^{t \ln [\ \ ]}$$

where [ ] stands for the expression between [ ] in (3.14.3). Integrating, we get

$$k^\lambda = \frac{\lambda\sigma P_0^\lambda}{\ln [\ \ ]} e^{t \ln [\ \ ]} + C \tag{3.14.4}$$

where C is an integration constant depending on the initial value of k.

It will be assumed that our units are so chosen as to make, for $t = 0$, $a_0 = k_0 = v_0 = P_0 = 1$.

Substituting $t = 0$ in (3.14.4), we obtain for C

$$C = 1 - \frac{\lambda\sigma}{\ln [\ \ ]}$$

and hence, for small values of ϵ and π,

$$k^\lambda = 1 + \frac{\lambda\sigma}{\epsilon + \lambda\pi} \{[(1+\epsilon)(1+\pi)^\lambda]^t - 1\} \tag{3.14.5}$$

It is clear that the time shape of k is, even in this case, less simple than most statistical methods of trend determination assume.

In order to study the influence exerted by the various data on the rate of development of production, we may rewrite Eq. (3.13.1) in logarithmic form:

$$\ln v = t \ln (1+\epsilon) + \lambda \ln P_0 + \lambda t \ln (1+\pi) + (1-\lambda) \ln k$$

differentiate it with respect to time,

$$\frac{\dot{v}}{v} = \ln (1+\epsilon) + \lambda \ln (1+\pi) + (1-\lambda)\frac{\dot{k}}{k} \tag{3.14.6}$$

apply it to time $t = 0$, use (3.13.8), and assume ϵ and π to be small,

$$\left(\frac{\dot{v}}{v}\right)_0 = \epsilon + \lambda\pi + (1-\lambda)\sigma$$

This equation is illuminating in that it shows the influence of the four constants ϵ, λ, π, and σ on the initial rate of growth. While the rate of increase in efficiency ϵ has a coefficient 1, the rate of population growth π has a coefficient λ and the propensity to save a coefficient $1 - \lambda$.

3.15 A general solution of the type (3.14.5) is less easily obtained if the supply of labor is not completely inelastic. It is possible, however, to obtain results of the type (3.14.6) for cases where λ and α have been given numerical values. Examples have been worked out for $\lambda = 3/4$, a value often quoted in statistical publications by Professor Douglas and his associates. Since very little is known about the supply elasticity of labor, various values have been assumed for it. The results are shown in Table 3.1.

TABLE 3.1. VALUES FOR $\dot{k}$, $\dot{a}$, AND $\dot{v}$ AT TIME $t = 0$, FOR VARIOUS VALUES OF α
($a = P_0 = k = v = 1$; $\lambda = 3/4$)

α	0	$1/2$	∞	-1
$\dot{k}$	σ	σ	σ	σ
$\dot{a}$	$\sigma + 4\epsilon - 4\Omega$	$\frac{\sigma}{3} + \frac{2}{3}\pi + \frac{4}{3}\epsilon - \frac{4}{3}\Omega$	π	$-\frac{\sigma}{3} + \frac{4}{3}\pi - \frac{4}{3}\epsilon + \frac{4}{3}\Omega$
$\dot{v}$	$\sigma + 4\epsilon - 3\Omega$	$\frac{\sigma}{2} + \frac{1}{2}\pi + 2\epsilon - \Omega$	$1/4\sigma + 3/4\pi + \epsilon$	$\pi + \Omega$

As presented here, the results are contributions to the solution of the analytical problem to explain the rate of growth in employment and production with the aid of such data as the rate of savings σ, the rate of growth ϵ of efficiency, the rate of growth π of the population, and the rate of increase Ω in desired wages. Interestingly enough, the results depend to a considerable extent on the supply elasticity of labor α. Even so, some general conclusions are possible, for example, that an acceleration in the growth of population (that is, an increase in π) will as a rule be accompanied by a lower acceleration in production, and by an equal acceleration in production only when $\alpha = -1$. Likewise, an acceleration in capital formation, that is, an increase in σ, will at most lead to an equal expansion in production and employment (for $\alpha = 0$), but as a rule to a smaller relative expansion.

The results may also be used for the solution of policy problems, for example, in order to determine the values of σ and Ω in order to obtain given rates of increase in production and employment. While using the table, the reader should be aware of the units in which the variables have been expressed (indicated in the table heading).

3.16 A few words may be added about the case in which

$$\lambda + \mu > 1 \tag{3.16.1}$$

The main difficulty which such a model presents is that incomes accruing to labor and to capital, respectively, add up to more than total national product. This points to the necessity to raise taxes from one or both of these groups, in order to cover the losses on the operation of such an economy, losses comparable to those incurred when production requires fixed costs. Another alternative is that employers act as monopolists vis-à-vis the factors of production, or as oligopolists, which is more likely. The case therefore requires a careful specification of the structural and institutional setup before it can be presented as a realistic picture of an economy as a whole.

Such a difficulty does not exist if $\lambda + \mu < 1$. Here, a profit remains in the hands of the organizers of production, which is a more realistic feature than a loss.

3.2. Models with Various Types of Technological Change

3.21 Before presenting some examples of models in this field, we must make a few general remarks on the concept of technological change and the appropriate instruments of analysis. Some instruments that are appropriate at a primitive stage of analysis lose their meaning in a more sophisticated approach. Whether such a sophisticated approach is applicable, however, depends on factual details.

By the primitive approach we mean the one which describes each individual process of production by the numerical inputs and outputs characterizing it. Taking capital and labor as the only inputs and considering the process the production of one unit of a certain product, we can represent each input combination by a point in a two-dimensional diagram, plotting the quantity of labor along the horizontal and the quantity of capital along the vertical axis (see Fig. 3). Process 1 will then be more labor-consuming and less capital-intensive than process 2, and the transition from process 1 to process 2 is a technological change characterized by saving labor, a laborsaving change, since $a_2 < a_1$. At the same time it requires more capital per unit of product, and we may also speak therefore of substitution of labor by capital. A pure case of laborsaving, in this context, would be a change from 1 to 3, where only $a_3 < a_1$, but $k_3 = k_1$. Clearly one could also conceive of pure capital-saving changes and of changes where capital is substituted by labor (for example, a change from 2 to 3 and one from 1 to 4).

Consideration of all individual processes is a rather cumbersome affair, with very restricted possibilities to generalize any results found. Of course the facts may be that way, and that cannot be helped. More powerful conclusions can be drawn if the facts obey a certain logical structure. An important feature of technological reality is that at any single moment not one single process to produce a given commodity is known, but often a set of them, which can be represented by a set of points in our diagram, for example, the set 2, 1, 4. In other cases, a continuous collection of processes may be known. In fact, even when only discrete processes are known, such as 2, 1, and 4, there is a continuous set of possibilities, since 2 and 1 can be carried out simultaneously in any proportion, meaning that all points of the line 12 are also technological possibilities. For various purposes, such a continuous set of points may be sufficiently approximated by a curve, often called the *curve of technological possibilities.*

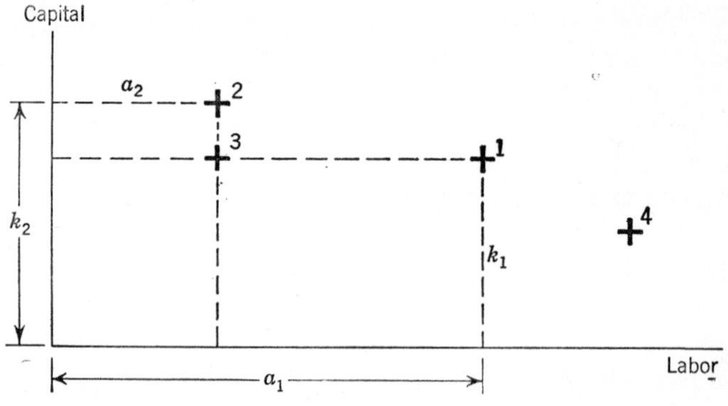

Fig. 3

The Cobb-Douglas curve is an example; for the unit of product it is represented, at any given time, by the formula

$$1 = \Gamma a^{\lambda} k^{1-\lambda} \tag{3.21.1}$$

or

$$\frac{1}{a} = \Gamma \left(\frac{k}{a}\right)^{1-\lambda} \tag{3.21.2}$$

In the last version, the left-hand side indicates labor productivity, and this appears to be a very simple function of capital per worker, or capital intensity.

If now, by a change in technological knowledge, the curve of technological possibilities shifts, we no longer have the possibility of speaking of laborsaving changes in the simple way we did before, since we cannot say that any particular point on the second curve corresponds to a given point on the first curve. The natural way to characterize the change is to indicate how the parameters of the curve, occurring in its formula, have changed. It depends on the number and nature of the parameters, how many types of change there are, and what their nature is. Appropriate names can then be given to each kind of change.

Since the Cobb-Douglas function is one of the very few production functions presented and tested so far, it makes sense first to study technological changes applying to that function. Since it contains two parameters in its simplest version (3.21.2), and three when the exponent of capital in its more general version (3.11.1) is left free, there are two or three types of changes to be distinguished.

We shall call a rise in Γ a *rise in general efficiency*, since it implies that the quantity of product obtained with the help of any combination of production factors increases in the same proportion. If such a rise occurs at a uniform rate, Γ can be given the form chosen in (3.11.1), namely $(1 + \epsilon)^t$.

The second type of change that may occur is a rise or fall in λ. The nature of a change in λ may be understood by a study of its consequences. Perhaps the most striking consequence of a fall in λ is that the portion of national product accruing to labor falls. In this sense the change means a saving in labor costs and may be called a laborsaving change. The phrase is not a happy one, however. It is more exact to speak of a fall in the *elasticity of production* with respect to labor, since λ simply is the elasticity and nothing else. It should be realized, at the same time, that changes in λ or μ do not always represent technological progress. Only changes in λ or μ or both, leaving an addition to the product, constitute progress. Such changes $d\lambda$ and $d\mu$ therefore must obey the condition

$$a^{\lambda+d\lambda}k^{\mu+d\mu} > a^{\lambda}k^{\mu}$$

or

$$d\lambda \ln a + d\mu \ln k > 0 \qquad (3.21.3)$$

3.22 We shall now indicate some consequences for economic development of a systematic change in λ and μ, characterized by the condition, previously adhered to, that $\lambda + \mu = 1$ and by the relation

$$\lambda = \lambda_0 + \lambda' t \qquad (3.22.1)$$

It is possible to apply the same method as in Sec. 3.15. The results in Table 3.2 are obtained.[1]

TABLE 3.2. VALUES FOR $\dot{a}$ AND $\dot{v}$ AT TIME $t = 0$ FOR VARIOUS VALUES OF α ($a = P_0 = k = v = 1$; $\lambda_0 = 3/4$)

α	0	½	∞	−1
$\dot{a}$	$\sigma - 16/3\lambda' + 4\epsilon - 4\Omega$	$\frac{\sigma}{3} - \frac{16}{9}\lambda' + \frac{2}{3}\pi + \frac{4}{3}\epsilon - \frac{4}{3}\Omega$	π	$-\frac{\sigma}{3} + \frac{16}{9}\lambda' + \frac{4}{3}\pi - \frac{4}{3}\epsilon + \frac{4}{3}\Omega$
$\dot{v}$	$\sigma - 4\lambda' + 4\epsilon - 3\Omega$	$\frac{\sigma}{2} - \frac{4}{3}\lambda' + \frac{1}{2}\pi + 2\epsilon - \Omega$	$1/4\sigma + 3/4\pi + \epsilon$	$4/3\lambda' + \pi + \Omega$

3.23 For practical purposes, it is interesting to answer the question what values of ϵ, a general rise in efficiency, and of λ', a shift in the elasticity of production with respect to labor, are realistic.

[1] Taken from H. Banerji, Technical Progress and the Process of Economic Development, *NUFFIC*, The Hague, 1956.

Over very long periods not very much of a change in λ has been observed: the distribution of income between labor and capital has long been one of a constant ratio. To be sure, this phenomenon has been accompanied by two other phenomena which should not be lost sight of: (1) a persistent reduction in the number of working hours and (2) a change in the relative numbers of workers and independent producers. The latter phenomenon implies that per capita incomes of workers and of the economy as a whole need not have moved in proportion.

A shift in Γ equivalent to a fairly regular increase in general efficiency has occurred, however, and roughly of the order of 1 per cent per annum. A check on this figure can be made with the aid of the empirical fact that the capital-output ratio has been roughly constant in some developed countries over about a century.

TABLE 3.3. SOME REALISTIC VALUES (IN PER CENT) OF λ, ω, AND π AND THE RESULTING VALUES OF ϵ REQUIRED IN ORDER THAT THE CAPITAL COEFFICIENT BE CONSTANT

ω	π	$\omega - \pi$	ϵ	
			$\lambda = 3/4$	$\lambda = 2/3$
4	1.5	2.5	1.9	1.7
4	1.0	3.0	2.3	2.0
4	0.5	3.5	2.6	2.3
3	1.5	1.5	1.1	1.0
3	1.0	2.0	1.5	1.3
3	0.5	2.5	1.9	1.7
2.5	1.5	1.0	0.8	0.7
2.5	1.0	1.5	1.1	1.0
2.5	0.5	2.0	1.5	1.3

Writing the Cobb-Douglas production function in its most general version (3.11.1), and assuming inelasticity in the labor supply, we can derive an expression for the capital-output ratio.

$$\kappa = \frac{k}{v} = P_0^{-\lambda} \frac{k^{1-\mu}}{(1+\epsilon)^t(1+\pi)^{\lambda t}} \tag{3.23.1}$$

In order that this ratio be constant over time, the fraction at the right-hand side must be constant; since capital and output have to move proportionately also, the rate of increase per annum of k must be ω (that is, the rate of increase in production). This requires that

$$\omega(1-\mu) = \epsilon + \lambda\pi \tag{3.23.2}$$

or

$$\epsilon = \omega(1-\mu) - \lambda\pi \tag{3.23.3}$$

If we assume that $\lambda + \mu = 1$, this reduces to

$$\epsilon = \lambda(\omega - \pi) \tag{3.23.4}$$

Some realistic values of λ, ω, and π have been summarized in Table 3.3, together with the resulting values of ϵ.

3.24 It is also possible to prove that, with the model discussed, the capital-output ratio has a tendency to become constant in the course of time. Starting from Eq. (3.13.1) and (3.14.4), we obtain for the capital-output ratio

$$\kappa = \frac{k}{v} = \frac{k^\lambda}{(1+\epsilon)^t P_0{}^\lambda (1+\pi)^{\lambda t}}$$

$$= \frac{\lambda\sigma}{\ln\,[(1+\epsilon)(1+\pi)^\lambda]} + \frac{C}{[(1+\epsilon)(1+\pi)^\lambda]^t P_0{}^\lambda \ln\,[\quad]}$$

which for growing values of t approaches the limit

$$\kappa_\infty = \frac{\lambda\sigma}{\ln\,[(1+\epsilon)(1+\pi)^\lambda]} \sim \frac{\lambda\sigma}{\epsilon + \lambda\pi} \tag{3.24.1}$$

This result[1] may be interpreted to mean that the constancy of the capital coefficient need not be considered a technical datum, but rather the result of a growth process. According to this formula, the capital coefficient depends on the two technical coefficients λ and ϵ, as well as on the rate of savings σ and the rate of population growth π. A high capital coefficient should be expected, according to this formula, in countries showing a high savings ratio and a low rate of population growth.

3.3. Models with Accounting Prices

3.31 Models of the type discussed in the preceding sections of this chapter may be used to estimate the influence of a *policy of accounting prices* for production factors. Such a policy is characterized by (1) the imposition on the public sector of a calculation system which uses accounting prices for labor and capital instead of market prices, and (2) the introduction, in the private sector, of a system of taxes and subsidies on the use of factors to induce private entrepreneurs to base their calculations on accounting prices also. If the accounting price of labor is lower than its market price, a subsidy will have to be offered, while a tax will be imposed wherever the accounting price is higher than the market price. It is proposed to estimate the effects of such a policy on employment, production, and development, as well as on public finance.

[1] Due to Professor P. J. Verdoorn; see The Role of Capital in Long-term Projection Models, *Cahiers écon.* (*Bruxelles*), vol. 1, p. 49, 1959.

Following Dr. A. Qayum,[1] we have assumed that accounting prices are applied only to new investments.

3.32 The variables used in the model are

- a total employment
- $\bar{a}$ employment in sector without accounting prices, to be called *nonaccounting sector*
- $\tilde{a}$ employment in sector under accounting prices, to be called *accounting sector*
- k total capital in use
- $\bar{k}$ capital used in nonaccounting sector
- $\tilde{k}$ capital used in accounting sector
- v national product
- l market wage rate
- l' accounting wage rate
- m market interest rate
- m' accounting interest rate
- G taxes (subsidies are considered negative taxes)
- Φ_1 labor-capital ratio in accounting sector
- Φ_0 labor-capital ratio without accounting prices

Development over time will be calculated for all these variables; it is assumed that the policy of accounting prices is introduced at time $t = 0$. The formulas will be so devised that they show the development at any level of accounting prices introduced; this level as well as the level of market prices will be assumed constant over time, however, implying that, without accounting prices, the endowment with capital and labor would have grown proportionately.

3.33 The relations of the model are: capital in the nonaccounting sector is assumed to diminish at a rate $\delta' = 1 - \delta$, where δ is the rate of depreciation of capital goods—treated as a constant percentage applied to the existing stock.

$$\bar{k}_t = \bar{k}_0 \delta'^t \tag{3.33.1}$$

Since the labor-capital ratio in the nonaccounting sector has been chosen on the basis of market prices, it remains at the same level; hence employment in this sector diminishes proportionately to capital.

$$\bar{a}_t = \bar{a}_0 \delta'^t \tag{3.33.2}$$

Capital in the accounting sector grows for two reasons: depreciation allowances are re-invested and new savings are invested in it.

$$\dot{\tilde{k}}_t = \delta \bar{k}_t + \sigma v_t \tag{3.33.3}$$

Here σ is the propensity to save, as before.

[1] A. Qayum, "Theory and Policy of Accounting Prices," Amsterdam, 1960.

Employment in the accounting sector remains in a fixed proportion to capital, because accounting prices remain fixed. This implies that we assume no technological change, that is, $\epsilon = 0$.

$$\tilde{a}_t = \Phi_1 \tilde{k}_t \tag{3.33.4}$$

Total production, and hence income, is composed of production in the two sectors; using the preceding equations, we get

$$v_t = \bar{a}_t^\lambda \bar{k}_t^{1-\lambda} + \tilde{a}_t^\lambda \tilde{k}_t^{1-\lambda} = \bar{a}_0^\lambda \bar{k}_0^{1-\lambda} \delta'^t + \Phi_1^\lambda \tilde{k}_t = v_0 \delta'^t + \Phi_1^\lambda \tilde{k}_t \tag{3.33.5}$$

Market wage rates are equal to marginal productivity of labor in the nonaccounting sector:

$$l = \lambda \left(\frac{\bar{k}_t}{\bar{a}_t}\right)^{1-\lambda} = \lambda \left(\frac{\bar{k}_0}{\bar{a}_0}\right)^{1-\lambda} = \lambda \Phi_0^{\lambda-1} \tag{3.33.6}$$

Market interest rates are equal to marginal productivity of capital in the nonaccounting sector:

$$m = (1-\lambda)\left(\frac{\bar{a}_t}{\bar{k}_t}\right)^\lambda = (1-\lambda)\Phi_0^\lambda \tag{3.33.7}$$

Accounting wage rates are equal to marginal productivity of labor in the accounting sector:

$$l' = \lambda \left(\frac{\tilde{k}_t}{\tilde{a}_t}\right)^{1-\lambda} = \lambda \Phi_1^{\lambda-1} \tag{3.33.8}$$

Accounting interest rates are equal to marginal productivity of capital in the accounting sector:

$$m' = (1-\lambda)\left(\frac{\tilde{a}_t}{\tilde{k}_t}\right)^\lambda = (1-\lambda)\Phi_1^\lambda \tag{3.33.9}$$

Taxes are equal to taxes on capital in the accounting sector minus subsidies on labor in that sector; both are proportional to the differences between accounting and market prices, whichever is higher, and to the quantities employed in the accounting sector:

$$G = (m' - m)\tilde{k}_t - (l - l')\tilde{a}_t \tag{3.33.10}$$

These ten equations determine the ten variables $\bar{a}$, $\tilde{a}$, $\bar{k}$, $\tilde{k}$, v, l, l', m, m', and G. If we so wish, a and k can be found from two additional balance equations:

$$a = \bar{a} + \tilde{a} \tag{3.33.11}$$
$$k = \bar{k} + \tilde{k} \tag{3.33.12}$$

3.34 The two problems we proposed to solve can easily be dealt with in the following way.

Combining Eqs. (3.33.3), (3.33.1), and (3.33.5), we obtain

$$\begin{aligned} \dot{\tilde{k}}_t &= \delta\delta'^t k_0 + \sigma(v_0\delta'^t + \Phi_1^\lambda \tilde{k}_t) \\ &= (\delta k_0 + \sigma v_0)\delta'^t + \sigma\Phi_1^\lambda \tilde{k}_t \end{aligned} \tag{3.34.1}$$

This is a nonhomogeneous differential equation of the first order in $\tilde{k}_t$; its general solution consists of two parts, I and II, where I is the general solution of the homogeneous equation

$$\dot{\tilde{k}}_t = \sigma\Phi_1{}^\lambda \tilde{k}_t \tag{3.34.2}$$

and II a particular solution of the nonhomogeneous equation (3.34.1). Solution I is:

$$\tilde{k}_t{}^{\mathrm{I}} = \tilde{K}_0{}^{\mathrm{I}} e^{\sigma\Phi_1{}^\lambda t} \qquad \tilde{K}_0{}^{\mathrm{I}} \text{ arbitrary} \tag{3.34.3}$$

For solution II assume that $\tilde{k}_t{}^{\mathrm{II}} = \tilde{K}_0{}^{\mathrm{II}}\delta'^t$. Then $\dot{\tilde{k}}_t{}^{\mathrm{II}} = \tilde{K}_0{}^{\mathrm{II}}\delta'^t \ln \delta'$; substituting into (3.34.1), we get

$$\tilde{K}_0{}^{\mathrm{II}} \ln \delta' = \delta k_0 + \sigma v_0 + \sigma\Phi_1{}^\lambda \tilde{K}_0{}^{\mathrm{II}}$$

from which it follows that $\tilde{K}_0{}^{\mathrm{II}}$ has to satisfy the condition

$$\tilde{K}_0{}^{\mathrm{II}} = \frac{\delta k_0 + \sigma v_0}{\ln \delta' - \sigma\Phi_1{}^\lambda} \tag{3.34.4}$$

Hence the general solution is

$$\tilde{k}_t = \tilde{K}_0{}^{\mathrm{I}} e^{\sigma\Phi_1{}^\lambda t} + \frac{\delta k_0 + \sigma v_0}{\ln \delta' - \sigma\Phi_1{}^\lambda}\,\delta'^t \tag{3.34.5}$$

The arbitrary constant $\tilde{K}_0{}^{\mathrm{I}}$ has to be found from the initial condition that for $t = 0$, $\tilde{k}_0 = 0$; this requires

$$\tilde{K}_0{}^{\mathrm{I}} = -\frac{\delta k_0 + \sigma v_0}{\ln \delta' - \sigma\Phi_1{}^\lambda} \tag{3.34.6}$$

Thus the solution becomes

$$\tilde{k}_t = \frac{\delta k_0 + \sigma v_0}{\sigma\Phi_1{}^\lambda - \ln \delta'}\,(e^{\sigma\Phi_1{}^\lambda t} - \delta'^t) \tag{3.34.7}$$

The denominator may be written approximately as $\sigma\Phi_1{}^\lambda + \delta$, since for small δ, $\ln \delta' = \ln (1 - \delta) = -\delta$.

The expression for $\tilde{k}_t$ is positively dependent on Φ_1, meaning that capital develops more quickly if Φ_1 is put higher, that is, if the accounting price for labor is put relatively low and the accounting price for capital relatively high. Since both employment and production are again positively dependent on $\tilde{k}_t$ and on Φ_1, all these variables will grow faster, the higher Φ_1 is. The limit set to this growth is evidently full employment of the labor force.

In order to determine the financial burden to the government, we combine Eqs. (3.33.10) and (3.33.6) to (3.33.9), yielding

$$G = (\Phi_1{}^\lambda - \Phi_0{}^\lambda + \lambda\Phi_0{}^\lambda - \lambda\Phi_0{}^{\lambda-1}\Phi_1)\tilde{k}_t \tag{3.34.8}$$

Writing $\Phi_1 = \varphi\Phi_0$, we find

$$G = (\varphi^\lambda - 1 + \lambda - \lambda\varphi)\Phi_0{}^\lambda \bar{k}_t \tag{3.34.9}$$

For values of φ slightly above 1 this is of second order only in $\varphi - 1$, meaning that as a first approximation taxes and subsidies are of equal size and that there is a very small net burden on the government. For values of φ well above 1 this is no longer so; thus, for $\varphi = 1.5$ and $\lambda = \frac{2}{3}$ we find

Tax on capital:	$\frac{1}{3}(1.5^{2/3} - 1)\bar{k}_t = 0.10\bar{k}_t$
Subsidy on labor:	$\frac{2}{3}(1.5 - 1.5^{2/3})\bar{k}_t = 0.12\bar{k}_t$
Net burden:	$-G = 0.02\bar{k}_t$

3.4. Models with Restricted Substitution between Factors

3.41 If the number of processes is small, there may be a point in specifying them exactly and in developing the various cases or configurations that may present themselves. This method recommends itself if the problems of a single industry with clearly distinct processes are at stake, or if the economy is of an extremely simple type. A good example of one industry in which these conditions prevail is Indian cotton weaving. Sometimes similar differences between large-scale and small-scale business may play a role. For a more complicated economy as a whole it is doubtful whether the method is of much help. Even if in a single industry there is a choice between two methods only, as a rule the choice between industries represents another possibility of choosing between capital-intensive and labor-intensive processes, and the number of possibilities may turn out to be large.

3.42 Let us consider two processes characterized by upper indexes 1 and 2, where 1 is the more labor-intensive process. The following variables will be considered.

a^1, a^2	employment in processes 1 and 2
k^1, k^2	capital used in processes 1 and 2
v^1, v^2	product obtained in the two processes
m^1, m^2	profit rates earned in the two processes
l	wage rate, supposed uniform

As data we shall consider

P	total population, as far as employable
k^0	total capital stock available
g^1, g^2	labor productivity in the two processes
κ^1, κ^2	capital coefficients of the two processes
$\bar{l}$	minimum wage level, by custom or law

3.43 We shall not study the models in this class in much detail but only briefly indicate the configurations conceivable, as mentioned. The relation with development planning is that these configurations may materialize in succession, if capital per head of the population moves along an upward trend. Over very long periods this may indeed be so. Most of our other planning models will refer to the period of capital scarcity and labor abundance, which is the common situation in underdeveloped countries, although not necessarily the only possible situation.

It appears that five configurations or phases may thus be distinguished.

I. All capital used in process 1, leaving still a surplus of labor
II. All capital used in process 1, supplying employment to all labor
III. Capital and labor distributed over both processes
IV. Capital and labor fully employed only in process 2
V. All labor employed in process 2, leaving some capital unused

Which of these configurations materializes evidently depends on the ratio k_0/P, the dependency being

Case I: $$\frac{k^0}{P} < \frac{k^1}{a^1} = \kappa^1 g^1$$

Case II: $$\frac{k^0}{P} = \kappa^1 g^1$$

Case III: $$\kappa^2 g^2 > \frac{k^0}{P} > \kappa^1 g^1$$

Case IV: $$\frac{k^0}{P} = \kappa^2 g^2$$

Case V: $$\frac{k^0}{P} > \kappa^2 g^2$$

The relationship can be shown most clearly in a graphic way:

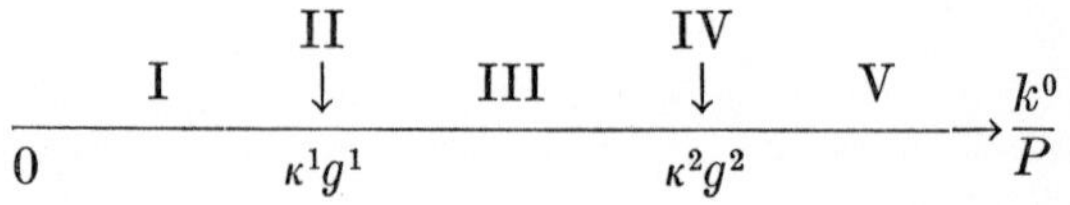

Under free competition of factors, the price of labor in case I and that of capital in case V would be zero. In case III, where there is coexistence of processes 1 and 2, wages will have to satisfy the condition $m^1 = m^2$ since otherwise capital would be withdrawn from one of the processes. This condition can be elaborated by using the definition of profit rates and of capital-output ratios.

$$m^1 = \frac{v^1 - la^1}{\kappa^1 v^1} = \frac{v^2 - la^2}{\kappa^2 v^2} = m^2 \qquad (3.43.1)$$

Since, in addition, $v^1 = g^1a^1$ and $v^2 = g^2a^2$, the condition becomes, expressed in terms of data,

$$m^1 = m^2 = m^{\text{III}} = \frac{g^1 - l}{\kappa^1 g^1} = \frac{g^2 - l}{\kappa^2 g^2}$$

or

$$l^{\text{III}} = g^1 g^2 \frac{\kappa^2 - \kappa^1}{\kappa^2 g^2 - \kappa^1 g^1} \tag{3.43.2}$$

In cases II and IV, wage and profit rates are, within certain limits, undetermined. With our assumption about a minimum wage $\bar{l}$, this will be a lower limit to l in case II. Evidently this implies that $\bar{l} < l^{\text{III}}$.

In case I, therefore, we have $l^{\text{I}} = \bar{l}$ and consequently

$$m^{\text{I}} = \frac{g^1 - \bar{l}}{\kappa^1 g^1}$$

In case V, we will have $m^2 = 0$ and hence $l^{\text{V}} = g^2$ unless there is some minimum set to m also.

3.44 Sometimes there may be scope to combine the ideas underlying Secs. 3.1 and 3.4 by assuming that within certain limits of k/a, continuous substitution is possible, whereas outside these limits no further substitution is possible.

3.5. The Role of Aims in the Design of Policy

3.51 The main subject of this book is the presentation of economic models which may be helpful in planning development. Models themselves do not say anything about the use that may be made of them, as was already set out in Chap. 1. In fact, very different policy devices may be obtained with the aid of the same model. This difference evidently depends on the aims set for a development policy. It may also depend on the means used or excluded. In this section we shall demonstrate by some examples how widely different policy devices may sometimes be obtained with the same model. We do so at this stage because the models we have been discussing are sufficient to make our point. It could be repeated later when more complicated models have been discussed, but then it would be a cumbersome affair, not adding very much to the clarity of exposition. We shall first treat some examples and finish with some conclusions (see Sec. 3.55).

3.52 In this section we use a one-sector one-factor model as discussed in Sec. 2.1. Our variables will be capital k_t, income y_t, and consumption c_t. Our initial position k_0 (and hence y_0) is given. The policy instrument considered is the rate of saving $\sigma = (y - c)/y$, supposed to be constant over time and to be chosen once forever. In order to show the influence of aims set, we choose consumption at different times as the aim of development: in Example 1, consumption now; in Example 2, consumption at some later time T; in example 3, total consumption over a period $0 \leq t \leq T$.

With our attention to be focused on consumption, it is useful to express the development of this variable over time in terms of the data of our problem. This can be done in the following way, if we remember that with a constant savings ratio σ all variables develop proportionately to $e^{(\sigma/\kappa)t}$ (see Sec. 2.13):

$$c_t = y_t - \dot{k}_t = \frac{k_t}{\kappa} - \dot{k}_t = \left(\frac{k_0}{\kappa} - \frac{\sigma}{\kappa} k_0\right) e^{(\sigma/\kappa)t} = \frac{k_0}{\kappa}(1 - \sigma)e^{(\sigma/\kappa)t} \tag{3.52.1}$$

Example 1. Consumption now

$$c_0 = \frac{k_0}{\kappa}(1 - \sigma) \tag{3.52.2}$$

This evidently becomes a maximum if we choose $\sigma = 0$; no savings, no development.

Example 2. Consumption at time T

$$c_T = \frac{k_0}{\kappa}(1 - \sigma)e^{(\sigma/\kappa)T} \tag{3.52.3}$$

This will be a maximum for $dc_T/d\sigma = 0$, or

$$\frac{T}{\kappa}(1 - \sigma)e^{(\sigma/\kappa)T} - e^{(\sigma/\kappa)T} = 0$$

$$\frac{T}{\kappa} - \frac{T}{\kappa}\sigma - 1 = 0$$

$$\sigma = \frac{T - \kappa}{T}$$

Since κ is around 3 years, we find, for some values of T,

$T =$	5	10	15	20
$\sigma =$	0.4	0.7	0.8	0.85

We also see that up to $T = 3$, the policy device obtained suggests no savings (taking into account the boundary condition that savings should not be negative) or even negative savings—supposing that we can dissave up to the amount of k_0.

Example 3. Consumption over period $0 \leq t \leq T$

$$\bar{c} = \frac{k_0}{\kappa}(1 - \sigma)\int_0^T e^{(\sigma/\kappa)t'}\,dt'$$

We can easily find

$$\bar{c} = \frac{k_0}{\sigma}(1 - \sigma)(e^{(\sigma/\kappa)T} - 1) \tag{3.52.4}$$

Upon differentiation and putting the derivative equal to zero, we obtain a transcendental equation in σ, which is not explicitly solvable. The simplest procedure to estimate σ is to try, for given numerical values of T and κ. It is easily seen that T and κ appear only in the combination T/κ; therefore it is only this that matters.

$\frac{T}{\kappa} =$ 0	0.55	1.4	2.0	2.1	2.3	2.4	2.6	2.7	3.5	5.3	∞
$\sigma = -\infty$	-5.4	-0.72	0	0.10	0.18	0.25	0.31	0.37	0.57	0.75	1

Figures up to $T/\kappa = 2$ do not make sense evidently and will have to be replaced by boundary conditions. The remaining figures show that, depending on the length of the period T, any savings figure can be found. Assuming $\kappa = 3$ years, we find that for $T = 7.2$ years, such a realistic figure as 18 per cent is the optimum rate of savings, but that for $T = 8.1$ years, we find already 37 per cent and for $Y = 16$ years, 75 per cent.

3.53 In this section we use a one-sector two-factors model with continuous substitution between factors, as discussed in Sec. 3.14, without the rise in general efficiency (the simplest Cobb-Douglas model). Initial capital k_0 is supposed given; so is the population P, not supposed to be fully employed during the period considered. Let the aim be income v_T at time T and the instrument the choice of technology, which may simply be represented by the number a employed with the capital available. For the sake of simplicity, we assume a to be constant, but other assumptions are possible as well.

Income $\quad v = a^\lambda k^{1-\lambda} \quad$ and $\quad \dot{k} = \sigma v = \sigma a^\lambda k^{1-\lambda} \quad$ (3.53.1)

This leads to $\quad k^\lambda = \lambda\sigma a^\lambda t + k_0{}^\lambda \quad$ (3.53.2)

and to $\quad v = a^\lambda k^{1-\lambda} = a^\lambda(\lambda\sigma a^\lambda t + k_0{}^\lambda)^{(1-\lambda)/\lambda} \quad$ (3.53.3)

It is clear that, at any time T, v_T will be larger the larger a is and that, for the model assumed, the most labor-intensive technology will be the best device. Here, then, there is no great influence of the aim chosen on the policy device.

3.54 In this section we use a one-sector two-factors model with a choice between two processes of production yielding different savings rates. The variables considered are product v^1 or v^2, employment a^1 or a^2, capital k^1 or k^2, and profit rate m. The data are

Capital coefficients: $\quad \kappa^1 > \kappa^2$

Labor productivities: $\quad g^1 > g^2$

Savings ratios: $\quad \sigma^1 > \sigma^2$

These savings ratios are ratios of savings to profits and not to total income; the profits are k^1m and k^2m and hence savings σ^1k^1m or σ^2k^2m. Finally, initial capital stock k_0 is given.

We assume that the aim is to maximize employment at time T, the policy instrument being the choice of technology.

Suppose that process 1 is chosen; then we have

Volume of production: $$v_t^1 = \frac{k_t^1}{\kappa^1} \tag{3.54.1}$$

Volume of employment: $$a_t^1 = \frac{v_t^1}{g^1} = \frac{k_t^1}{\kappa^1 g^1} \tag{3.54.2}$$

Profits are $k_t^1 m$, savings $\sigma^1 k_t^1 m$, and hence

$$\dot{k}_t^1 = \sigma^1 k_t^1 m$$

yielding $$k_t^1 = k_0 e^{\sigma^1 m t} \tag{3.54.3}$$

It follows that employment at time T is

$$a_T^1 = \frac{k_0 e^{\sigma^1 m T}}{\kappa^1 g^1} \tag{3.54.4}$$

Since $\kappa^1 g^1 > \kappa^2 g^2$, employment at time $t = 0$ will be larger if process 2 is chosen. Since, however, $\sigma^1 > \sigma^2$, capital and hence employment will grow faster if process 1 is chosen. From a certain value of T on, therefore, process 1 will yield maximum employment. Again it depends on which time T is chosen whether one process or the other has to be selected.

3.55 Some provisional conclusions may be drawn from the examples presented and from general experience about related subjects. Clearly the most important conclusion is that a precise formulation of the aims of development is necessary in order to narrow down the range of uncertainty in the choice of policy instruments. The practical importance of this conclusion can be illustrated by mentioning some examples of the wide divergencies among policies adopted in different countries. We have already mentioned the large differences in the rate of savings. A second example is that of the large differences in trade policy and the choice of industries connected with it. Whereas some countries try to develop export industries in order to have the full advantage of the international division of labor, other countries develop import-replacing industries and tend toward autarchy. The remarkable trend from the latter toward the former point of view in the communist countries may be noted. A third example finally is the famous discussion about the choice of technology, in which some authors favor the establishment of capital-intensive and others labor-intensive industries. Whereas our last section (3.54) shows that again the aim chosen influences the answer, our next preceding section (3.53), in comparison with 3.54, also shows that the details of the model sometimes matter. Thus in this particular problem much depends on whether investments are financed out of savings made from profits or out of other sources, for example, taxes. In case they depend on taxes, they are connected with income as a whole and not only with profits; and the method of production yielding the maximum initial income will be the best one.

Important as a more precise formulation of aims may be, it still does not follow that such a formulation is sufficient to remove divergencies. As we have discussed previously, economic science is not yet able, to cite an important example, to solve the problem of the optimum rate of development (see Sec. 2.4). How much less will practical policy arguments be able to settle some of the biggest differences!

Chapter 4

SEVERAL SECTORS; FIXED PRICES; NO SUBSTITUTION

4.1. Models without Interindustry Deliveries

4.11 In this chapter, models will be discussed in which the economy is subdivided into a number of sectors, each characterized by a group of products or by one product. We shall deal with the subject by the method of *decreasing abstraction*, that is, we start with very simple models and gradually make them more complicated. In this chapter prices will be assumed fixed, that is, invariable. The conditions under which this assumption is justified have been discussed in Sec. 1.55. Moreover, the hypothesis will be made that substitution of one commodity group for another in no way occurs, neither on the side of demand or consumption nor on that of supply or production. Finally, in this first section, no interindustry deliveries will be supposed to exist. Although this assumption may never materialize completely, it will often apply approximately, in particular if the sectors represent vertically integrated combinations of activities. It will be assumed, however, that there is one *capital good* needed for the production of all sectors.

To begin with, a *closed* economy will be studied.

Sectors will be indicated throughout this book by an upper index h running from 1 to H. In the models with one capital good only, this good will have $h = 1$.

4.2. Closed Economy; One Capital Good

4.21 The variables of the model are

v^h volume of production of commodity h $(h = 1, \ldots, H)$
c^h volume of consumption of commodity h

s savings
j investment
y income

4.22 The relations of the model are

$$j = \sum_h \frac{\kappa^h}{\theta} (v^h_{t+\theta} - v^h) \tag{4.22.1}$$

Investment is equal to the sum of the quantities of the capital good needed by each sector for its future expansion. In this equation θ represents the gestation period, taken equal for all sectors; κ^h the capital-output ratio for sector h.

$$s = j \tag{4.22.2}$$

Investment is assumed to be financed from savings.

$$s = \sigma y \tag{4.22.3}$$

Savings are a given proportion of income, where σ is the propensity to save.

$$y = \sum_h v^h \tag{4.22.4}$$

Income equals the sum total of all production.

$$v^h = c^h \qquad h = 2, \ldots, H \tag{4.22.5}$$
$$v^1 = j \tag{4.22.5'}$$

Production, in the absence of exports and of interindustry deliveries, equals consumption for goods 2, . . . , H and investment for good 1.

$$c^h = \gamma^h(y - s) + \tilde{c}^h \qquad (h = 2, \ldots, H) \tag{4.22.6}$$
$$c^1 = 0 \tag{4.22.6'}$$

Consumption depends linearly on income minus savings and is zero for good 1. Here, γ^h are marginal propensities to consume and $\tilde{c}^h$ are intercepts of the Engel curves. We shall assume that total consumption adds up to income minus savings and that consumption cannot be negative. This means that the constants γ^h and $\tilde{c}^h$ must satisfy the following conditions:

$$\sum_h \gamma^h = 1 \tag{4.22.7}$$

$$\sum_h \tilde{c}^h = 0 \tag{4.22.8}$$

$$c^h \geq 0 \tag{4.22.9}$$

As a consequence, there may be, for various intervals of the variable $y - s$, different sets of coefficients γ^h and $\tilde{c}^h$.

Another consequence is that one of the equations, for example (4.22.2), is dependent on the others. The total number of independent equations therefore amounts to $2H + 3$ and equals the number of variables.

4.23 As always, the model can be used for the solution of various problems. In this section, we shall concentrate on the problem of planning development with a given value of σ, based perhaps on the considerations presented in Chap. 2. The model then serves to determine the development of the various sectors which is compatible with the given value of σ. This problem constitutes one of the simplest examples of the second stage of planning after σ has been determined in a first stage. This second stage supplies us with the relative sizes of the sectors, which, in their turn, enable us to calculate such average coefficients as the average capital-output ratio, assumed at a certain value in the macromodel used in stage 1. The second stage may thus lead to a value of the average capital-output ratio different from the one assumed before. If necessary a second round of stages in planning can then be undertaken.

4.24 The *nature of the solution* may first be illustrated by an example in which $H = 3$ and $\theta = 1$. The system of equations can be reduced to equations containing the v^h only as unknowns; in this particular case, they are, for $t = 0$

$$v_1^2 = \gamma^2(1 - \sigma)(v_1^1 + v_1^2 + v_1^3) + \bar{c}^2 \qquad (4.24.1)$$

$$v_1^3 = \gamma^3(1 - \sigma)(v_1^1 + v_1^2 + v_1^3) + \bar{c}^3 \qquad (4.24.2)$$

$$\sigma(v_0^1 + v_0^2 + v_0^3) = \kappa^1(v_1^1 - v_0^1) + \kappa^2(v_1^2 - v_0^2) + \kappa^3(v_1^3 - v_0^3) \qquad (4.24.3)$$

4.25 For the *special case* where $\kappa^1 = \kappa^2 = \kappa^3 = \kappa$, we can write the system in the form

$$v_1^2 = \gamma^2(1 - \sigma)y_1 + \bar{c}^2$$

$$v_1^3 = \gamma^3(1 - \sigma)y_1 + \bar{c}^3$$

$$\sigma y_0 = \kappa(y_1 - y_0) \qquad \text{or} \qquad y_1 = \left(1 + \frac{\sigma}{\kappa}\right) y_0$$

Here, the third equation is identical with the corresponding relation in a Domar-Harrod model, yielding the development over time of y; the first and second equation then yield the individual v's.

4.26 The system (4.24.1) to (4.24.3) is a *generalization*. The last equation may now be written

$$\sigma y_0 = (y_1 - y_0) \sum_h \kappa^h \frac{v_1^h - v_0^h}{y_1 - y_0} \qquad (4.26.1)$$

This means that we can still handle the model as a Domar-Harrod macromodel if we define

$$\kappa = \sum_h \kappa^h \frac{v_1^h - v_0^h}{y_1 - y_0} \qquad (4.26.2)$$

that is, if we make κ a weighted average of the κ^h with variable weights $(v_1{}^h - v_0{}^h)/(y_1 - y_0)$. Since the unknowns are appearing in the weights, this is not a solution in the mathematical sense, but constitutes a hint for practical approximations.

4.27 The *exact solution* can be undertaken along the following lines. We solve the system (4.24.1) to (4.24.3) for the v_1 by first writing it

$$\begin{aligned} -\gamma^2(1-\sigma)v_1{}^1 + [1-\gamma^2(1-\sigma)]v_1{}^2 - \gamma^2(1-\sigma)v_1{}^3 &= \tilde{c}^2 \\ -\gamma^3(1-\sigma)v_1{}^1 - \gamma^3(1-\sigma)v_1{}^2 + [1-\gamma^3(1-\sigma)]v_1{}^3 &= \tilde{c}^3 \\ \kappa^1 v_1{}^1 + \kappa^2 v_1{}^2 + \kappa^3 v_1{}^3 &= (\kappa^1+\sigma)v_0{}^1 + (\kappa^2+\sigma)v_0{}^2 + (\kappa^3+\sigma)v_0{}^3 \end{aligned} \tag{4.27.1}$$

From the first two equations we can derive $v_1{}^2$ and $v_1{}^3$ as linear functions of $v_1{}^1$ without any lag. Substituting in the third equation, we find, for $\boldsymbol{v}_1{}^1$, a linear expression in

$$(\kappa^1+\sigma)v_0{}^1 + (\kappa^2+\sigma)v_0{}^2 + (\kappa^3+\sigma)v_0{}^3 = \Sigma(\kappa^h+\sigma)v_0{}^h$$

this being the only combination of initial values $v_0{}^h$ which we have to know in order to find all future values of all variables.

The formulas so far discussed can be conveniently used for *numerical extrapolation.*

4.28 Since only one combination of initial values $\Sigma(\kappa^h+\sigma)v_0{}^h$ has to be given in order to determine the future movement, the *general mathematical solution*[1] will contain one arbitrary constant only, reflecting the fact that our system (4.24.1) to (4.24.3) can be replaced by a final equation of the first order. This is due to the facts that (1) we have one capital good only and (2) the gestation periods are all equal to one. The general mathematical solution consists in assuming

$$v_t{}^h = \bar{v}_0{}^h e^{\omega t} + \bar{v}^h \qquad h = 1, 2, 3 \tag{4.28.1}$$

and trying this solution out. Substituting it into the system (4.27.1) we shall get two types of terms, namely, terms proportional to $e^{\omega t}$ and constant terms. In order that the solutions satisfy the equations, the following conditions must be fulfilled:

$$\text{(I)}\quad \begin{aligned} -\gamma^2(1-\sigma)\bar{v}_0{}^1 + [1-\gamma^2(1-\sigma)]\bar{v}_0{}^2 - \gamma^2(1-\sigma)\bar{v}_0{}^3 &= 0 \\ -\gamma^3(1-\sigma)\bar{v}_0{}^1 - \gamma^3(1-\sigma)\bar{v}_0{}^2 + [1-\gamma^3(1-\sigma)]\bar{v}_0{}^3 &= 0 \\ \kappa^1\bar{v}_0{}^1 + \kappa^2\bar{v}_0{}^2 + \kappa^3\bar{v}_0{}^3 &= [(\kappa^1+\sigma)\bar{v}_0{}^1 \\ &\quad + (\kappa^2+\sigma)\bar{v}_0{}^2 + (\kappa^2+\sigma)\bar{v}_0{}^3]e^{-\omega} \end{aligned}$$

$$\text{(II)}\quad \begin{aligned} -\gamma^2(1-\sigma)\bar{v}^1 + [1-\gamma^2(1-\sigma)]\bar{v}^2 - \gamma^2(1-\sigma)\bar{v}^3 &= \tilde{c}^2 \\ -\gamma^3(1-\sigma)\bar{v}^1 - \gamma^3(1-\sigma)\bar{v}^2 + [1-\gamma^3(1-\sigma)]\bar{v}^3 &= \tilde{c}^3 \\ \kappa^1\bar{v}^1 + \kappa^2\bar{v}^2 + \kappa^3\bar{v}^3 &= (\kappa^1+\sigma)\bar{v}^1 \\ &\quad + (\kappa^2+\sigma)\bar{v}^2 + (\kappa^3+\sigma)\bar{v}^3 \end{aligned}$$

The first set (I) originates from the terms in $e^{\omega t}$ and the second (II) from the constant terms. From II we find that the $\bar{v}^h$ are uniquely determined

[1] See, e.g., William J. Baumol, "Economic Dynamics," pp. 151ff., New York, 1959.

by the additive constants $\bar{c}^h$ and the coefficients of the system of equations, that is, by the structural constants.

Conditions (I) are linear homogeneous in the $\bar{v}_0{}^h$, meaning that, on the one hand, one of them can be chosen arbitrarily and that, on the other hand, their coefficients have to obey the condition that their determinant is zero.

$$\begin{vmatrix} -\gamma^2(1-\sigma) & 1-\gamma^2(1-\sigma) & -\gamma^2(1-\sigma) \\ -\gamma^3(1-\sigma) & -\gamma^3(1-\sigma) & 1-\gamma^3(1-\sigma) \\ \omega'\kappa^1-(\kappa^1+\sigma) & \omega'\kappa^2-(\kappa^2+\sigma) & \omega'\kappa^3-(\kappa^3+\sigma) \end{vmatrix} = 0 \qquad (4.28.2)$$

where ω' has been written for e^{ω}.

This condition determines ω', and since ω' occurs only in the last line, the equation is linear in ω' and has one root only. This fits with our previous finding that the general solution contains only one arbitrary constant.

This constant must be so determined that the only expression in the values $v_0{}^h$ which occurs in the system (4.27.1), namely, $\sum_h (\kappa^h + \sigma)v_0{}^h$, assumes the correct numerical value. This is not the usual situation in systems of equations of the type considered, but represents what mathematicians call a *degeneration*, as a consequence of the absence of lagged variables in the first two equations of (4.27.1). We shall deal with the usual, more general case later, when we are no longer assuming the existence of one capital good only. The fact just explained has a very interesting economic implication. Even when the values $v_0{}^1$, $v_0{}^2$, $v_0{}^3$ do not fit the demand equations (4.22.5) and hence do not fit the *pattern of balanced growth* as defined by our equations, the values for $t = 1$, that is, $v_1{}^1$, $v_1{}^2$, $v_1{}^3$, will fit already. Although in more general models we shall meet the phenomenon of a *transition or adaptation period*, during which the economy, in a few steps, approaches this pattern, this adaptation takes place in one time unit—being the gestation period—here. As mentioned in this section, such an adaptation is possible in one time unit only if we have one capital good and a gestation period of one unit.

The models to be discussed later will, step by step, be made more complicated. It seemed useful, however, to treat this simple situation first. The reader will have no difficulties in removing the restriction to three sectors only; this may be suggested as an exercise.

4.3. Models with Second-order Capital Goods

4.31 Important practical problems arise from the fact that capital goods are often *specific*, that is, can be used only for one or a few related production processes. In particular, if a switch in general development policy is aimed at, for example, in order to develop one sector less quickly than foreseen and another sector more quickly, considerable difficulties may come up, because some capital goods cannot be used for the purposes now aimed at.

So far this problem has not been recognized in our models. In the one-sector models of Chaps. 2 and 3, all goods have been considered interchangeable. We have only spoken of *production* and assumed that any portion of this production could be *saved*, making it part of the country's capital stock. In some models discussed in this chapter, capital goods have been considered interchangeable: their supply could be used in one sector or another. As long as capital grows, no difficulties arise. If, however, production in some sectors should fall, there would be difficulties. Suppose the volume of savings should be lowered. This means that less capital goods and more consumer goods would have to be produced and that, correspondingly, less capacity in the capital goods industry would be needed. As another example, assume that production in one sector of consumer goods should be lowered and in another sector raised. In both cases, capital goods would be in surplus in some sector and short in another. Our formulas tacitly assumed that a transfer was possible. If the goods are specific, this is not correct, however, and our formulas apply only if all capacities are rising, or, at most, falling by no more than annual depreciation. It may be said in defense of our formulas that development planning, which is the purpose for which our models are built, does not require, as a rule, reductions in capacity. This is not true for adaptation periods, however; nor is it true for the sectors producing so-called inferior goods.

Two attitudes are possible in the face of this problem. Surplus capital goods may be left idle, or they may be used for further production, as long as they are available. The former attitude requires a distinction, in our models, between capacity to produce and actual production, a distinction not made so far. We shall present a simple example of such a treatment (see Sec. 4.35). The latter attitude implies that the adaptation process is retarded as a consequence of specificity of capital goods. In this section, an example of this coincidence will be discussed (see Sec. 4.36).

Before dealing with these examples, we shall discuss another implication of specificity of capital goods.

4.32 As soon as capital goods are assumed to be specific, it becomes necessary to distinguish between capital goods to produce consumer goods and capital goods to produce capital goods. In a well-known terminology, the former may be called *first-order capital goods*, leaving another category which could then be called *second-order capital goods*.

There may well be scope even to introduce higher orders too. It is interesting to note that a strict adherence to the concept of specificity would force us to make one of two assumptions: either the highest-order capital goods can be produced without the aid of further capital goods, that is, with the aid of labor only, or there is an infinite number of *orders*. Both are unrealistic, the latter assumption even inconsistent with the existence of capital goods. A more realistic assumption is that for some order specificity no longer applies. The simplest assumption evidently is that this applies already to second-order capital goods. Thus, for example, we may assume that there are two types of capital goods, looms and lathes. Looms are specific and can only produce textiles (representing consumer goods) and lathes are not: they can be used for producing looms or for producing more lathes. In this train of thought there are two sectors producing capital goods, one producing looms, the other producing lathes, but their capacities can be switched. Statistically perhaps the nearest approximation to lathes is the product group of machine tools.

4.33 We shall now analyze the consequences of the introduction of second-order capital goods for the general process of development as brought out by some of the simplest models. It is not necessary to distinguish between different sorts of consumer goods, and in this respect our models will be similar to those presented in Chaps. 2 and 3. In the first model, without gestation periods, the *variables* are

- v^1 production of first-order capital goods (looms)
- v^2 production of second-order capital goods (lathes)
- v^3 production of consumer goods (textiles)
- v total production, equal to income

The *relations* are

$$v^1 = \kappa^3 \dot{v}^3 \tag{4.33.1}$$

The production of first-order capital goods is proportional to the rate of increase in consumer-goods production; κ^3 is the capital-output ratio in the consumer-goods industry.

$$v^2 = \kappa^1 \dot{v}^1 + \kappa^2 \dot{v}^2 \tag{4.33.2}$$

The production of second-order capital goods is the sum total of the production for loom making and lathe making, both depending on the rate of increase in the production of these two items, the coefficients being the capital-output ratios for producing looms (κ^1) and lathes (κ^2), respectively.

$$v^3 = (1 - \sigma)v \tag{4.33.3}$$

The production of consumer goods equals their demand, which equals income minus savings.

$$v = v^1 + v^2 + v^3 \tag{4.33.4}$$

Income is equal to the sum total of all production figures.

4.34 The general solution of the equations just presented will yield us the rate of increase in production that can be obtained from a given rate of savings σ. The solution appears to be simple: by substituting (4.33.3) into (4.33.1) and (4.33.1) into (4.33.2) we obtain

$$v^2 = \kappa^1\kappa^3(1 - \sigma)\ddot{v} + \kappa^2\dot{v}^2 \tag{4.34.1}$$

Substituting (4.33.3) into (4.33.1) and both into (4.33.4) yields

$$v = \kappa^3(1 - \sigma)\dot{v} + v^2 + (1 - \sigma)v \tag{4.34.2}$$

or

$$v^2 = \sigma v - \kappa^3(1 - \sigma)\dot{v} \tag{4.34.3}$$

It follows that

$$\dot{v}^2 = \sigma\dot{v} - \kappa^3(1 - \sigma)\ddot{v} \tag{4.34.4}$$

which can be substituted into (4.34.1):

$$\sigma v - [(1 - \sigma)\kappa^3 + \sigma\kappa^2]\dot{v} + \kappa^3(\kappa^2 - \kappa^1)(1 - \sigma)\ddot{v} = 0 \tag{4.34.5}$$

As a possible solution[1] we try $v = v_0e^{\omega t}$, implying that $\dot{v} = \omega v_0 e^{\omega t}$ and $\ddot{v} = \omega^2 v_0 e^{\omega t}$. Substituting in (4.34.5), we find that ω must satisfy

$$\sigma - [(1 - \sigma)\kappa^3 + \sigma\kappa^2]\omega + \kappa^3(\kappa^2 - \kappa^1)(1 - \sigma)\omega^2 = 0 \tag{4.34.6}$$

This equation has two roots which are rather complicated expressions in the coefficients κ^1, κ^2, κ^3, and σ. For some special cases it is easy, however, to determine them. Thus, for $\kappa^2 = \kappa^1$, the last term in (4.34.6) vanishes, and there is only one root $\omega = \sigma/\kappa$, if $\kappa = (1 - \sigma)\kappa^3 + \sigma\kappa^2$, that is, a weighted average of κ^3 and κ^2 with weights $(1 - \sigma)$ and σ. This is the result Domar-Harrod models yield.

For $\kappa^3 = \kappa^2 = \kappa$ and $\kappa^2 - \kappa^1 = \Delta\kappa$ we have

$$\sigma - \kappa\omega + \kappa\,\Delta\kappa(1 - \sigma)\omega^2 = 0 \tag{4.34.7}$$

For small values of σ we can solve this equation explicitly and find two roots:

$$\omega_1 = \frac{\sigma}{\kappa} \qquad \omega_2 = \frac{1}{\Delta\kappa(1 - \sigma)} - \frac{\sigma}{\kappa} \tag{4.34.8}$$

The first root corresponds to a Domar-Harrod process with the value κ as the relevant capital-output ratio.

The second root may assume high numerical values, pointing to the possibility of a high rate of growth. Further analysis shows, however, that the corresponding process of quick growth cannot last long under

[1] See, e.g., Kells, *loc. cit.*

the assumption made with regard to σ, namely, the assumption of a constant σ. This constitutes a difference in comparison with the simplest Domar-Harrod model discussed before, where σ can take any constant value.

The question may then be asked what other behavior is compatible with the technical relations in the present model. One of the simplest patterns conceivable is a pattern with a constant proportion of new investment devoted to the production of looms.[1] This assumption implies the replacement of Eq. (4.33.3) by another one running

$$\dot{v}^1 = \varphi \dot{v}^2 \tag{4.33.3'}$$

with

$$0 \leq \varphi \leq \infty \tag{4.34.9}$$

It can be shown that development now satisfies the equation

$$v_t = v_0{}^1 + v_0{}^3 - \varphi v_0{}^2 \frac{\kappa^3\kappa^1\varphi + \kappa^3\kappa^2 + 1}{\kappa^3(\kappa^1\varphi + \kappa^2)} + \frac{v_0{}^1 - \varphi v_0{}^2}{\kappa^3} t + \left[\frac{\varphi}{\kappa^3(\kappa^1\varphi + \kappa^2)} + 1 + \varphi\right] v_0{}^2 e^{\frac{t}{\kappa^1\varphi + \kappa^2}} \tag{4.34.10}$$

The rate of development ω is no longer a constant now; it is highest for $\varphi = 0$ and asymptotically approaches $\omega_\infty = 1/\kappa^2$.

It may be left to the reader to qualify this statement.

4.35 A very simple model will now be discussed in which the capacity to produce enters as a variable alongside production. Let there be two sectors, indicated by superscripts 1 and 2, producing consumer goods and capital goods, respectively. The variables of the model are

k^1 capital-goods stock in sector 1
k^2 capital-goods stock in sector 2
v^1 production of consumer goods
v^2 production of capital goods

The relations are

$$k^h \geq \kappa^h v^h \qquad h = 1, 2 \tag{4.35.1}$$

Production can at most be equal to capital-goods stock divided by capital-output ratio.

$$v^1 = (1 - \sigma)(v^1 + v^2) \tag{4.35.2}$$

Production of consumer goods is equal to demand, being equal to income minus savings.

$$v_t{}^2 = \sum_h (k_{t+1}^h - k_t{}^h) \tag{4.35.3}$$

[1] See also Sec. 5.1.

Production of capital goods is equal to the sum total of the rates of increase, after the gestation period, of capital-goods stocks in both industries.

The model is underdetermined under some circumstances. But it is clear that the initial values of k^1 and k^2, namely, k_0^1 and k_0^2, can be such that full utilization of these capacities (that is, $k^1 = \kappa^1 v^1$ and $k^2 = \kappa^2 v^2$) is incompatible with a given value of σ requiring that

$$\frac{v^1}{v^2} = \frac{1 - \sigma}{\sigma}$$

In such a case full utilization can exist in only one sector—in sector 1, if

$$\frac{k^2/\kappa^2}{k^1/\kappa^1} > \frac{\sigma}{1 - \sigma}$$

and in sector 2 if

$$\frac{k^2/\kappa^2}{k^1/\kappa^1} < \frac{\sigma}{1 - \sigma}$$

4.36 The discrepancies just described will present themselves when a sudden change in σ is introduced. Thus, assuming that σ has been 0.1 for some time, we have

$$v^1 : v^2 = \frac{1 - \sigma}{\sigma} = 9$$

In order to fix the ideas let us take $\kappa^1 = 2$ and $\kappa^2 = 4$. If $\sigma = 0.1$ for a succession of years already, the economy has been able to adapt itself to it, and hence we shall have

$$k^1 : k^2 = \kappa^1 v^1 : \kappa^2 v^2 = 4\tfrac{1}{2}$$

and according to (4.35.3)

$$\frac{k_{t+1}^1 - k_t^1}{k_{t+1}^2 - k_t^2} = 4\tfrac{1}{2}$$

also. If at a certain moment t_0 total capital amounts to 11 units, we have $k_{t_0}^1 = 9$, $k_{t_0}^2 = 2$.

Suppose now the government wants, in the future, σ to be 0.2 and hence $(1 - \sigma)/\sigma = 4$, implying that in future equilibrium $k^1 : k^2 = 2$. If capital goods in the two sectors were interchangeable, the stock of 11 could be redistributed between the two sectors so as to obey this condition, that is, $k^1 = \tfrac{2}{3} \times 11 = 7\tfrac{1}{3}$ and $k^2 = 3\tfrac{2}{3}$. If, however, this interchangeability does not exist, k^1 will have to remain 9, and all the economy can do is, for some time to come, to use all production v^2 to increase k^2—meaning that σ is only changed by steps. Since for $t = t_0$, $v^2 = \tfrac{2}{4} = \tfrac{1}{2}$, during that year k^2 can be brought only to the level of $2\tfrac{1}{2}$, and for the subsequent years we have the following figures if all v^2 is used to increase k^2:

t	k^2	v^2 (rounded)	k^1/k^2	v^1/v^2	σ_t
$t_0 + 1$	2.5	0.63	3.6	7.2	0.122
$t_0 + 2$	3.13	0.78	2.88	5.76	0.148
$t_0 + 3$	3.91	0.98	2.30	4.60	0.178
$t_0 + 4$	4.89				

Evidently at time $t_0 + 3$, we have not yet reached the proportion $k^1:k^2 = 2:1$, but at time $t_0 + 4$, we have surpassed the goal, meaning that during period $t_0 + 3$ we could have devoted part of v^2 to increasing k^1, the correct policy being determined by the equations

$$k^1_{t_0+4} - k^1_{t_0+3} + k^2_{t_0+4} - k^2_{t_0+3} = 0.98$$
$$k^1_{t_0+3} = 9 \qquad k^2_{t_0+3} = 3.91$$
$$k^1_{t_0+4} = 2k^2_{t_0+4}$$

The result is $k^1_{t_0+4} = 9.26$, and $k^2_{t_0+4} = 4.63$.

The example illustrates that it takes 4 time units now to reach a path compatible with the new policy. As a consequence of the specificity of capital goods, we have an adaptation period even in this simple model with only one gestation period.

At the same time it will be clear that for small changes in σ there is no need for an adaptation period. Let us calculate what is the maximum change in σ for which no adaptation period is necessary. Evidently this change must be such that by devoting the whole of v^2 to one type of capital goods we can, in period t_0, just reach the composition of capital corresponding to the new value of σ. Since $v^2 = \frac{1}{2}$, the extreme situations are

(1) $$k^1_{t_0+1} = 9 \qquad k^2_{t_0+1} = 2.5 \qquad \text{and} \qquad \frac{k^1}{k^2} = 3.6$$

(2) $$k^1_{t_0+1} = 9.5 \qquad k^2_{t_0+1} = 2 \qquad \text{and} \qquad \frac{k^1}{k^2} = 4.75$$

The corresponding values of $(1 - \sigma)/\sigma = 2k^1/k^2$ are

(1) $$\frac{1 - \sigma}{\sigma} = 7.2 \qquad \text{with} \qquad \sigma = 0.122$$

(2) $$\frac{1 - \sigma}{\sigma} = 9.5 \qquad \text{with} \qquad \sigma = 0.095$$

Therefore, for the new σ' obeying $0.122 \geq \sigma' \geq 0.095$, there is no need for an adaptation period.

4.37 A final remark on methodology seems in order. As the reader will have observed, the problems discussed can most elegantly be handled by giving a central role to the variables k^1 and k^2, or generally all the components of the capital stock. This is the way a number of problems of this type—and considerably more complicated—have been dealt with in mathematico-economic publications.[1]

4.4. Open Economy; One Capital Good

4.41 The variables of the model are

v^h volume of production of commodity h ($h = 1, \ldots, H$)
c^h volume of consumption
e^h volume of exports (negative values of e^h representing imports)
s savings
j investment
y income

4.42 The relations of the model are Eqs. (.1), (.2), (.3), (.4), and (.6) of model 4.22, plus a number of relations indicating the development over time of exports, for example,

$$e^h = e_0{}^h + \bar{e}_1{}^h t \qquad (4.42.1)$$

These equations express, in a very simple way, the limitations upon an expansion of exports, often felt to be very real in underdeveloped countries.

In addition we have a relation replacing (.5) of model 4.22:

$$v^h = c^h + e^h \qquad h = 2, \ldots, H \qquad (4.42.2)$$
$$v^1 = j + e^1 \qquad (4.42.2')$$

4.43 In order to have a clear understanding of the logical implications of the number of such relations we may first derive a side condition from Eqs. (4.22.4), (4.42.2), (4.42.2′), (4.22.2), and (4.22.6), having in mind (4.22.7) and (4.22.8).

$$y = \sum v^h = \sum_2^H c^h + \sum_1^H e^h + j = y - s + s + \sum e^h$$

$$\therefore \sum e^h = 0 \qquad (4.43.1)$$

This side condition brings out the well-known identity of internal financial equilibrium and balance-of-payments equilibrium. It implies that one of the e^h follows from the others.

As long as there is only one import item, Eq. (4.43.1) expresses the fact that these imports are determined by exports. If there are more import items, we are confronted with the difficulty that equations of the

[1] See R. Dorfman, P. A. Samuelson, and R. M. Solow, "Linear Programming and Economic Analysis," New York, 1958.

type (4.42.1) do not make much sense for import items. Condition (4.43.1) will then not be sufficient to determine each import item, and the model becomes underdetermined. A realistic way out will sometimes be the assumption that some of the sectors are *empty*, meaning, as we have seen, that no production takes place. In such a sector, imports have to be equal to consumption (in this simple model). In terms of supplementary relations it means that for empty sectors we have

$$v^h = 0 \tag{4.43.2}$$

4.44 Imports of goods which are also produced at home represent essentially a case of substitution and will not be considered in this chapter. We therefore assume that the number of empty sectors is equal to the number H^I of import items, minus one. This makes the number of relations equal to

	1	(4.22.1)
	1	(4.22.2)
	1	(4.22.3)
	1	(4.22.4)
	H	(4.22.6)
	H^E (number of export items)	(4.42.1)
	H	(4.42.2) and (4.42.2′)
	$H^I - 1$	(4.43.2)
Total	$2H + H^E + H^I + 3$	

The variables add up to this same total and the model is, as a rule, determinate.

The *nature of the solution* of the planning problem with given value of σ may again be shown by taking the special case $H = 3$, $\theta = 1$. We assume that sector 1 is importing (but not empty) and that sectors 2 and 3 are exporting. Again, we may eliminate all variables except v^h, as in Sec. 4.27; the result is

$$\begin{aligned}
-\gamma^2(1-\sigma)v_1^1 + [1-\gamma^2(1-\sigma)]v_1^2 - \gamma^2(1-\sigma)v_1^3 &= \bar{c}^2 + e_0^2 + \bar{e}_1^2 t \\
-\gamma^3(1-\sigma)v_1^1 - \gamma^3(1-\sigma)v_1^2 + [1-\gamma^3(1-\sigma)]v_1^3 &= \bar{c}^3 + e_0^3 + \bar{e}_1^3 t \\
\kappa^1 v_1^1 + \kappa^2 v_1^2 + \kappa^3 v_1^3 = (\kappa^1+\sigma)v_0^1 &+ (\kappa^2+\sigma)v_0^2 + (\kappa^3+\sigma)v_0^3
\end{aligned} \tag{4.44.1}$$

The difference with system (4.27.1) clearly is that the equations are now, in the mathematician's language, nonhomogeneous difference equations.[1] The solutions found in Sec. 4.28 have to be supplemented now by

[1] See, e.g., Baumol, *op. cit.*, p. 175.

a particular solution of the nonhomogeneous equations. Such a particular solution may be given the form

$$v_t^h = \varphi_0^h + \bar{\varphi}^h t \tag{4.44.2}$$

and values for φ_0^h and $\bar{\varphi}^h$ can be found without difficulty by substituting (4.44.2) into (4.44.1). They are uniquely determined by the structural constants of the model. The general solutions will be [see Eq. (4.28.1)]

$$v_t^h = \bar{v}_0^h e^{\omega t} + \varphi_0^h + \bar{\varphi}^h t \tag{4.44.3}$$

since the constants $\bar{v}^h$ shown in (4.28.1) are now absorbed in φ_0^h. The movements of e^2 and e^3 will therefore, generally speaking, influence those of v^h and hence those of y. The influence on y will be rather weak since v^1, v^2, and v^3 are influenced in opposite directions as a consequence of $\Sigma e^h = 0$. In special *degenerated* cases the influence on y may even be absent; this is true for $\kappa^1 = \kappa^2 = \kappa^3$ again, for then the third equation is one in y, independent of the movements of the individual v^h, as in Sec. 4.25.

4.5. Input-Output Models with Uniform Lags; One Capital Good

4.51 We are now going to introduce the phenomenon of inter-industry deliveries. These constitute one important form of complementarity, a somewhat more general phenomenon of great importance to planning. In fact, the assumption that for the production of any commodity certain inputs of other different commodities are necessary is another way of stating that these various inputs are complementary. To the extent that we base our planning figures on such relationships, we do take account of such complementarities. It evidently depends on the details of the model used whether all relevant complementarities are taken account of. Thus it may happen that the necessary complementarity between the number of motor cars and the width of the roads is neglected.

In the examples to be discussed we shall, to begin with, maintain the assumption that there is only one capital good. We shall demonstrate the new features with the help of models for a closed economy; the reader will be able to apply them to open economies along the lines of Sec. 4.4.

4.52 The variables of the model are

v^h volume of production of commodity h
$v^{hh'}$ quantity of good h supplied to sector h', for current production of good h'
c^h consumption of good h
s savings
j investment
y income

4.53 The relations are those of Sec. 4.22, duly amended, supplemented with one set of new relations about interindustry deliveries. For the reader's convenience they are all given.

$$j = \sum_h \frac{\kappa^h}{\theta} (v^h_{t+\theta} - v^h) \tag{4.53.1}$$

$$s = j \tag{4.53.2}$$

$$s = \sigma y \tag{4.53.3}$$

$$y = \sum_h v^h - \sum_h \sum_{h'} v^{hh'} \tag{4.53.4}$$

This equation, the income definition, has been amended, since inputs used in the production of the various sectors must be deducted from gross product in order to obtain net product or income.

$$v^h = c^h + \sum_{h'} v^{hh'} \qquad h = 2, \ldots, H \tag{4.53.5}$$

$$v^1 = j$$

These equations, the balance equations, have also become more complicated now. Total production v^h now is composed of production for final consumption plus production for interindustry deliveries.

$$c^h = \gamma^h(y - s) + \bar{c}^h \qquad h = 2, \ldots, H \tag{4.53.6}$$

$$c^1 = 0 \tag{4.53.6$'$}$$

$$v^{hh'} = \varphi^{hh'} v^{h'} \tag{4.53.7}$$

This is the new set of technical equations expressing the assumption that inputs are proportional to outputs, with the technical coefficients $\varphi^{hh'}$ considered given. We shall consider somewhat more general relationships later.

4.54 The main application of the model will be for planning the sector production figures, once a value for σ has been chosen. As in Sec. 4.2, we may again easily obtain equations for v^h by the elimination of all other variables. These equations are somewhat more complicated but not essentially different from those obtained in Sec. 4.2. They may be summarized as follows:

$$v^h = \gamma^h(1 - \sigma) \sum_{h'} \left(1 - \sum_{h''} \varphi^{h''h'}\right) v^{h'} + \bar{c}^h + \sum_{h'} \varphi^{hh'} v^{h'} \tag{4.54.1}$$

$$\sigma \sum_h \left(1 - \sum_{h'} \varphi^{h'h}\right) v^h = \sum_{h'} \frac{\kappa^{h'}}{\theta} (v^h_{t+\theta} - v_t{}^h) \tag{4.54.2}$$

Since their mathematical shape is the same as before, all that was said about the nature of the solution applies.

4.6. Input-Output Models with Uniform Lags; Several Capital Goods

4.61 We now remove the restriction that there is only one capital good. Instead we recognize that almost all commodities can, in certain circumstances, play the role of capital goods. This is true in particular if we go into the details of inventory accumulation as a form of investment. This new approach, then, does not make the distinction between capital goods and other goods, but the distinction between two types of operation: current production and investment or the extension of production capacity. Accordingly, there are two input-output matrices of coefficients. We still stick to the assumption of uniform lags, that is, that the gestation periods for investments in all sectors are equal.

4.62 The list of variables now becomes

v^h production of good h
$v^{hh'}$ quantity of good h used in current production of h'
$w^{hh'}$ quantity of good h used to extend capacity of sector h'
c^h consumption of good h
s savings
y income

4.63 The list of relations will be

$$w^{hh'} = \frac{\kappa^{hh'}}{\theta}(v_{t+\theta}^{h'} - v_t^{h'}) \tag{4.63.1}$$

The new setup makes it necessary to introduce the new coefficients $\kappa^{hh'}$, to be called *partial capital coefficients* for investment of good h into sector h'.

$$s = \sum_h \sum_{h'} w^{hh'} \tag{4.63.2}$$

$$s = \sigma y \tag{4.63.3}$$

$$y = \sum_h v^h - \sum_h \sum_{h'} v^{hh'} = \sum_h v^h - \sum_{h'} \sum_h v^{h'h} \tag{4.63.4}$$

It is useful to state that the inputs $w^{hh'}$ for investment must not be deducted here. They represent dispositions of income spending rather than costs to current production as the $v^{hh'}$ are.

$$v^h = c^h + \sum_{h'} v^{hh'} + \sum_{h'} w^{hh'} \tag{4.63.5}$$

Production now is directed to three different purposes and, for open economies, even to four: consumption, current interindustry deliveries, such deliveries for investment purposes, and, in an open economy, exports (or, negatively, imports).

$$c^h = \gamma^h(y - s) + \bar{c}^h \tag{4.63.6}$$

This equation now also applies to $h = 1$.

$$v^{hh'} = \varphi^{hh'}v^{h'} \tag{4.63.7}$$

We can write the income definition in a shorter form,

$$y = \sum_h \varphi^{0h}v^h = \sum_h y^h \tag{4.63.4$'$}$$

by the introduction of the symbol

$$\varphi^{0h} = 1 - \sum_{h'} \varphi^{h'h} \tag{4.63.4$''$}$$

Here, y^h is income derived from sector h.

It should be kept in mind that the $H + H^2$ terms of y are grouped here according to receiving sectors and not to supplying sectors. This latter arrangement could be presented by a definition equation

$$y = \sum_h \left(v^h - \sum_{h'} v^{hh'}\right) = \sum_h \bar{v}^h \tag{4.63.4$'''$}$$

where $\bar{v}^h$ is the net quantity available for consumption, investment, and exports. Depending on the problems we have to solve, we shall use one or the other grouping in what follows.

4.64 Although the model can be used, as always, for different purposes, we shall illustrate its use by considering the problem of planning production of the sectors for a succession of years, once the savings ratio σ has been chosen. As in our previous examples, it is easy to eliminate all other variables and we are left with the system (for a closed economy)

$$v^h = \gamma^h(1 - \sigma) \sum_{h'} \varphi^{0h'}v^{h'} + \bar{c}^h + \sum_{h'} \varphi^{hh'}v^{h'} + \sum_{h'} \frac{\kappa^{hh'}}{\theta} (v^{h'}_{t+\theta} - v_t^{h'}) \tag{4.64.1}$$

The difference with system (4.27.1) is that the differences $v^{h'}_{t+\theta} - v_t^{h'}$ now occur in each equation; as a consequence the logical structure of the system becomes more complicated, leading to the planning problem of the *adaptation period*, already mentioned in Sec. 4.28. We solve Eq. (4.64.1) for $v^h_{t+\theta}$ and, for the sake of convenience, take $\theta = 1$. The solution may be written

$$v^h_{t+1} = \sum_{h'} \chi^{hh'}v_t^{h'} + \bar{\chi}^h \tag{4.64.2}$$

where the χ's are functions of the coefficients and additive structural constants appearing in (4.64.1).

Before continuing our mathematical argument we shall find it useful to explain in economic terms what these equations mean: how is it that, given the production volumes in period t, those of the subsequent period $t + 1$ are determined? The explanation is that the given volumes of production require given current inputs and hence fix current income. Income determines savings and quantities demanded for consumption of each commodity. Thus there remain quantities to be invested. With given—and different—proportions, in which, for each sector, investment inputs have to be combined, there will be, as a rule, only one way of using up all quantities of goods available for investment. It is for this reason that the future production pattern follows from the present one. Evidently a determinacy develops that is caused by the completely rigid production functions. Because of various substitution possibilities, to be discussed in later chapters, reality is not this rigid. Yet the model is a useful exercising ground and does bring out a number of problems of real life connected with complementarities.

4.65 In order to solve the planning problem under these circumstances, we shall, as usual, try a solution of the shape

$$v^h = \bar{v}_0{}^h e^{\omega t} + \bar{v}^h = \bar{v}_0{}^h \omega'^t + \bar{v}^h \tag{4.65.1}$$

where, in a somewhat loose way, ω may be called the rate of growth of the system and, for small ω, $\omega' \sim 1 + \omega$. Upon substituting these expressions into (4.64.2), we shall again find two types of terms, namely, constant terms and terms depending on t. In order that the assumed solution (4.65.1) satisfies, relation (4.64.2) must be satisfied identically by both types of terms separately. Similar to conditions (I) and (II) in Sec. 4.28, we get two sets of conditions here too; corresponding to (II) we have, for the constant terms,

$$\bar{v}^h = \sum_{h'} \chi^{hh'} \bar{v}^h + \bar{\chi}^h \tag{4.65.2}$$

From these equations the $\bar{v}^h$ can be determined as functions of the structural constants.

The conditions corresponding to (I) again are linear homogeneous in the $\bar{v}_0{}^h$, meaning that one factor for the whole set remains arbitrary and that, simultaneously, the determinant of the coefficients must vanish. This now takes the form

$$\begin{vmatrix} \chi^{11} - \omega' & \chi^{12} & \cdots & \chi^{1H} \\ \chi^{21} & \chi^{22} - \omega' & \cdots & \cdots \\ \cdots & \cdots & \cdots & \cdots \\ \chi^{H1} & \chi^{H2} & \cdots & \chi^{HH} - \omega' \end{vmatrix} = 0 \tag{4.65.3}$$

Contrary to the previous situation this is now an equation of the Hth degree, which, as a rule, will have H roots. There is not one value ω', therefore, but there are H values ω'_h satisfying (4.65.3), and the general solution for v_t^h runs

$$v_t^h = \sum_{h'} \bar{v}_{h'} \bar{v}^h_{0h'} \omega'^t_{h'} + \bar{v}^h \qquad \bar{v}^1_{0h'} = 1 \tag{4.65.4}$$

Here the roots ω' have been given a number h'; the general solution of v_t^h consists of the sum of the solutions corresponding to each ω', each solution containing a general multiplication factor $\bar{v}_{h'}$, equal for all v_t^h, and a relative value of $\bar{v}^h_{0h'}$, which has been chosen 1 for v_t^1 in all cases h'. The $\bar{v}^h_{0h'}$ are functions of the χ and $\omega'_{h'}$, but the $\bar{v}_{h'}$ are arbitrary and must be used to let the solutions fit the initial values of the variables, which must be given in order to make the problem a definite one.

4.66 So far what we have said about the solution of our problem applies just as well to the usual *analytical economic problem* of finding the future development of an economy with given initial values of the variables. In the case now considered, with gestation periods of one unit everywhere, these initial values will be v_0^h ($h = 1, \ldots, H$). It is clear that, with these values given, all future values of v_t^h can be calculated (numerically) from Eq. (4.64.2).

Generally speaking, however, the movements so found, and represented by Eq. (4.65.4), will show various components, of which only one is a smooth trend, the others being fluctuations of different periods and damping degrees. These movements will usually be considered undesirable by the planner. An additional complication is that our equations do not give a reliable picture of short-term reactions of free economic decisions and therefore the short-term fluctuations corresponding with the ω''s will be inaccurate forecasts.[1] The *planning problem therefore is not identical with the forecasting problem, but rather consists in producing, by the additional use of instruments of economic policy, a smooth development of the economy*, that is, a development along the paths

$$v_t^h = \bar{v}_1 \bar{v}^h_{01} \omega'^t_1 + \bar{v}^h \qquad \bar{v}^1_{01} = 1 \tag{4.66.1}$$

where ω'_1 represents the real root of (4.65.3) > 1.

The nature of the problems involved may be made clear by an example; we assume that $H = 3$ again. The initial values given to us by history are v_0^1, v_0^2, v_0^3. If, to begin with $t = 0$, we based our planning and our development policy on Eq. (4.64.2), that is, the system discussed in

[1] This is largely due to the fact that the acceleration principle, which is the core of long-term development, is a very inaccurate presentation of short-term reactions of a free economy.

Sec. 4.63 and summarized in Eq. (4.64.1), we would not necessarily obtain a *smooth* movement: the ratios between v_0^1, v_0^2, and v_0^3 may prevent this. For the movement to be smooth it would have to obey (4.66.1), which contains *one* arbitrary constant $\bar{v}_1$ only, and this cannot, as a rule, be chosen so as to satisfy the three conditions

$$\begin{aligned} v_0^1 &= \bar{v}_1 + \bar{v}^1 \\ v_0^2 &= \bar{v}_1\bar{v}_{01}^2 + \bar{v}^2 \\ v_0^3 &= \bar{v}_1\bar{v}_{01}^3 + \bar{v}^3 \end{aligned} \tag{4.66.2}$$

Only if our initial values happened to satisfy these relations would the problem of adaptation not exist.

We must therefore, if we wish to obey Eq. (4.66.1) later, deviate from Eq. (4.64.2) for some time, to be called the adaptation period; the questions to be answered are: how long and how must we deviate? The answers depend on the instruments available to the authorities to let the variables deviate. Taking up Eqs. (4.63.1) to (4.63.7) one by one, we find that Eqs. (.1), (.4), (.5), and (.7) because of their nature cannot be violated by additional government instruments. It may be possible to deviate from Eq. (.2), however, by importing foreign capital, from Eq. (.3) by imposing taxes used for forced savings, and from Eq. (.6) by specific taxes on some goods or by rationing.

4.67 We shall discuss three different examples with regard to the number of instruments. In example (1) we assume that the number of additional instruments is $H - 1$, that is, in the present context 2. To fix the ideas, we indicate them by Δs, being an additional term at the right-hand side of (4.63.3), to be called forced savings, and Δc^1, to be added to the equation for c^1, belonging to (4.63.6). As a consequence, Eq. (4.64.2) will have one additional term each.

$$\begin{aligned} v_{t+1}^1 &= \chi^{11}v_t^1 + \chi^{12}v_t^2 + \chi^{13}v_t^3 + \bar{\chi}^1 + \Delta\bar{\chi}^1(\Delta s, \Delta c^1) \\ v_{t+1}^2 &= \chi^{21}v_t^1 + \chi^{22}v_t^2 + \chi^{23}v_t^3 + \bar{\chi}^2 + \Delta\bar{\chi}^2(\Delta s, \Delta c^1) \\ v_{t+1}^3 &= \chi^{31}v_t^1 + \chi^{32}v_t^2 + \chi^{33}v_t^3 + \bar{\chi}^3 + \Delta\bar{\chi}^3(\Delta s, \Delta c^1) \end{aligned} \tag{4.67.1}$$

The values of $\Delta\bar{\chi}^h$ ($h = 1, 2, 3$) follow from those of Δs and Δc^1. With these additional terms we can see to it that for $t = 0$, the values of v_1^1, v_1^2, and v_1^3 obey conditions comparable to (4.66.2), namely

$$\begin{aligned} v_1^1 &= \bar{v}_1\omega_1' + \bar{v}^1 \\ v_1^2 &= \bar{v}_1\bar{v}_{01}^2\omega_1' + \bar{v}^2 \\ v_1^3 &= \bar{v}_1\bar{v}_{01}^3\omega_1' + \bar{v}^3 \end{aligned} \tag{4.67.2}$$

The three variables Δs, Δc^1, and $\bar{v}_1$ are at the planner's disposal to satisfy (4.67.2), and by applying Δs and Δc^1, the government can bring about the economy in the configuration, warranting a smooth development without an adaptation period. The difference with our example in Sec. 4.28 is that no special measures were even required then.

In example (2) we assume that the number of additional instruments is $>H - 1$, namely 3, for example, Δs, Δc^1, and similarly Δc^2. Not only can the adaptation problem be solved then also without delay, but there is even 1 degree of freedom left, meaning that the *level* $\bar{v}_1$, from which the smooth development starts, can be chosen (within limits, of course).

In example (3), on the contrary, we assume that the number of instruments is $<H - 1$, namely 1, say Δc^1 only. Clearly the problem cannot now be solved without delay; but it can be solved for $t = 1$, that is, for v_2^1, v_2^2, and v_2^3. By applying in two consecutive time periods 0 and 1, values Δc_0^1 and Δc_1^1, respectively, we can influence the values v_1^1, v_2^1, and v_3^1. Writing down (4.67.1) for $t = 1$ and $\Delta s = 0$, we then have

$$v_2^1 = \chi^{11}v_1^1(\Delta c_0^1) + \chi^{12}v_1^2(\Delta c_0^1) + \chi^{13}v_1^3(\Delta c_0^1) + \bar{\chi}^1 + \Delta\bar{\chi}^1(\Delta c_1^1)$$

etc., symbolizing that we have 2 degrees of freedom. These can in fact be used to satisfy conditions for v_2^h similar to (4.67.2).

In a general way we can conclude from our examples that with a number of instruments equal to n, the delay will be equal to the next lower integer of the fraction $(H - 1)/n$.

4.7. Input-Output Models with Different Lags

4.71 To assume uniform gestation periods for the various sectors is far from realistic. All economies show wide variations in such periods. Many important irrigation and power projects, as well as mining projects, require periods of several or many years for their completion. Therefore it seems appropriate to introduce this feature into our models too. The alternative treatment is to break up a long process into a series of shorter ones and to introduce such commodities as semifinished or even three-tenths-finished irrigation dams, which can only be outputs from or inputs into one single process. It does not make much difference which alternative is chosen; we shall introduce the former rather than the latter. Our formulas can be easily adapted since we have already used the symbol θ, which may now be replaced by θ^h.

4.72 The set of θ^h appearing in any model may be called, together with the $w^{hh'}$, the time structure of investment. As a rule, the time structure will have to be replaced by some simpler pattern, though not by the extremely simple pattern of only one lag. Therefore, it will be very helpful to approximate it by a set of multiples of one unit lag, preferably one year.

Even so, the structure may be very different in different cases. To let the reader understand how to tackle the resulting problems the best method seems to us to be the treatment of an example with some remarks about possibilities to generalize the results. We shall treat the simplest conceivable example, consisting of a model of two sectors only, showing gestation periods of $\theta^1 = 1$ and $\theta^2 = 2$ years.

4.73 The equations in v^h, comparable to (4.64.2), will now be

$$\begin{aligned} v^1_{t+1} &= \chi^{11}v_t{}^1 + \chi^{12}v_t{}^2 + \bar{\chi}^1 \\ v^2_{t+2} &= \chi^{21}v_t{}^1 + \chi^{22}v_t{}^2 + \bar{\chi}^2 \end{aligned} \tag{4.73.1}$$

From these equations it is clear that the initial values which we must know in order to determine the future course of the variables, say from $t = 1$ onward, are the three combinations

$$\chi^{11}v_0{}^1 + \chi^{12}v_0{}^2,\ \chi^{21}v^1_{-1} + \chi^{22}v^2_{-1},\ \chi^{21}v_0{}^1 + \chi^{22}v_0{}^2$$

Correspondingly, if we apply the standard method of general solution, we find a third-degree equation for ω', comparable to Eq. (4.65.3),

$$\begin{vmatrix} \chi^{11} - \omega' & \chi^{12} \\ \chi^{21} & \chi^{22} - \omega'^2 \end{vmatrix} = 0 \tag{4.73.2}$$

The general mathematical solution will be of the shape

$$v_t{}^h = \sum_1^3{}^{h'} \bar{v}_{h'}\bar{v}^h_{0h'}\omega'^t_{h'} + \bar{v}^h \tag{4.73.3}$$

with the $\bar{v}_1$, $\bar{v}_2$, $\bar{v}_3$ arbitrary and $\bar{v}^1_{01} = \bar{v}^1_{02} = \bar{v}^1_{03} = 1$ [see Eq. (4.65.4)]. Again, only one of these components will be desirable, and accordingly, additional instruments of economic policy may be required, and an adaptation period may be unavoidable.

4.74 The procedure can be easily generalized for more complicated cases. The degree of the equation for ω' will no longer be H, as in the case of a uniform lag of one time unit, but $\sum_h \theta^h$, where all θ^h's are assumed to be integers. This implies that the number of components and the number of initial values will be $\sum_h \theta^h$ too. With a number of additional instruments equal to n, there may be an adaptation period if the next lower integer to $\Sigma\theta^h/n$ is >0. The period will be equal to that integer.

It might be expressly stated that in the case of a uniform lag of two years, all the phenomena discussed will be at play also. The point is that with a two-year period the variables may show fluctuations which are among the undesirable components.

4.8. Input-Output Models with Variable Coefficients

4.81 The basic assumption of input-output technique in its present form is the constancy of the coefficients. This means that coefficients do not change over time and that they do not depend on the variables of the system. In this section some possibilities will be discussed to remove constancy over time. There are a few important examples of changes over time. Perhaps the most important example is the well-known continual fall in labor-input coefficients. Energy inputs are another example, and there are more of them. The fall in labor inputs is very marked in young industries, where it has been found that there may be a more or less general type of *learning curve* independent of the type of industry considered.

The removal of the other form of nonconstancy, that is, the introduction of coefficients depending on the variables of the system, surpasses the limits set for the present chapter. Some aspects of it will be discussed in the next chapter.

4.82 Coefficients changing over time do not constitute any difficulty to the operation called *numerical extrapolation*, illustrated by Sec. 4.28 and equally applicable to (4.44.1) and to (4.54.1) and (4.54.2). There is no difficulty indeed in changing the coefficients in each successive calculation. For practical planning purposes this method is sufficient, however, only if the model is a very simple one, requiring no adaptation by the use of additional instruments of economic policy.

4.83 A second method of dealing with the problem consists in writing the coefficients as explicit functions of time and linearizing all equations. This procedure will transform Eqs. (4.64.2) into equations of the following structure:

$$v_{t+1}^h = \sum_{h'} ({\chi_1}^{hh'} {v_t}^{h'} + {\chi_2}^{hh'} t) + \bar{\bar{\chi}}^h \qquad (4.83.1)$$

where ${\chi_1}^{hh'}$, ${\chi_2}^{hh'}$, and $\bar{\bar{\chi}}^h$ depend on the old coefficients $\chi^{hh'}$ and $\bar{\chi}^h$, on the initial values of the $v^{h'}$, and on the rates of change of the old coefficients. For the details of transformations of this kind the reader may be referred to textbooks on econometrics.

The result is a system of equations of the shape of (4.44.1), the solution of which was discussed in Sec. 4.44 [see Eq. (4.44.3)]. This solution can be used only for short intervals, the length of which depends on the rate of change of the coefficients.

4.84 A third method that may sometimes be useful is the method known in physics as the method of invertible changes. It applies to slow changes only in the coefficients. It consists in using the solutions of the case with constant coefficients and substituting for these coefficients the functions of time they are supposed to be. Thus, for the problem dealt with in Sec. 4.6 (input-output models with uniform lags and several capital goods), it means maintaining the general form (4.65.4) or (4.66.1) of the solutions, but substituting for the ω_h' the functions of time they become, once the $\chi^{hh'}$ are no longer constants but functions of time. To be sure, this can be done explicitly only in a small number of cases. For some problems implicit functions or numerical approximations of functions may also be useful, however.

Chapter 5

SEVERAL SECTORS; FIXED PRICES; SUBSTITUTION

5.1. Model with Substitution between Factors

5.11 In Sec. 1.56, we discussed briefly various types of substitution playing a role in modern economies. Of those, intertemporal substitution is so much the core of the development problem that it finds treatment in every chapter of this book. Substitution between factors was dealt with in Chap. 3, without distinguishing between products. We shall take up this subject again in this chapter, in a model with several sectors (see Secs. 5.12ff.).

A third form of substitution is the one possible through international trade. This will be the subject of a few models for *open* countries, to be taken up in Secs. 5.2 and 5.3.

A fourth type of substitution is the substitution open to the consumer. Although this may be effectuated by such quantitative devices as rationing, it is more customary and more attractive to let prices play a role. This is why the subject will be taken up in Chap. 6, where prices are introduced as variables.

Although the models of Secs. 5.1 to 5.3 use the methods of input-output analysis, there is scope for using the more complicated method of linear programming for a number of the problems under discussion. This will be undertaken in Chap. 6. In this chapter, we shall treat finally some nonlinear relationships between inputs and outputs which can be considered to constitute examples of substitution also (Secs. 5.5 and 5.6).

Introducing the element of substitution in one way or another means increasing the degrees of freedom of the policy maker. While the only degree of freedom in the models of Chap. 4 was the rate of saving, which we assumed to be determined already, these models actually had no degree of freedom except the *additional instruments of economic policy* introduced in Sec. 4.6. In the present chapter, there are more degrees of freedom. This means that planning can be determinate only after further aims of economic policy have been defined. The problems to be presented as examples of the use of the models will be based on the further aim of maximizing national income to be obtained each year with the aid of the capital available.

5.12 In this subsection we discuss first a two-sector model, developed by Professor P. C. Mahalanobis.[1] The model considers a closed economy and distinguishes two sectors, sector 1 producing investment goods, sector 2 consumer goods only. The increase in production is dependent on the investments made in each sector. The policy problem discussed with the help of this model is how to allocate between the two sectors the investment goods produced.

5.13 The *variables* of the model are

c volume of consumption goods produced (by sector 2)
j volume of investment goods produced (by sector 1)
w^{11} volume of investment goods used to increase the production capacity in sector 1
w^{12} volume of investment goods delivered to sector 2
y national income

5.14 The *equations* of the model are the following:

$$\Delta c = \zeta^{12} w^{12} \tag{5.14.1}$$

This is an alternative formulation of similar equations discussed in Sec. 4.6, the coefficient ζ^{12} being equal to $1/\kappa^{12}$ and the investment lag being equal to one time unit. Thus

$$w_t^{12} = \kappa^{12}(c_{t+1} - c_t) \tag{5.14.1'}$$

$$\Delta j = \zeta^{11} w^{11} \tag{5.14.2}$$

Similarly, this equation expresses the increase in the production of investment goods that is made possible by an increase in the production capacity of the investment-goods industry.

$$w^{12} = \Lambda^{12} j \tag{5.14.3}$$

$$w^{11} = \Lambda^{11} j \tag{5.14.4}$$

These equations express the allocation of total investments between the two sectors. The coefficients Λ^{11} and Λ^{12} are instruments of economic policy and add up to 1: $\Lambda^{11} + \Lambda^{12} = 1$.

[1] Some Observations on the Process of Growth of National Income, *Sankhyā*, vol. 12, p. 307, 1953; and The Approach of Operational Research to Planning in India, *Sankhyā*, vol. 16, p. 3, 1955.

$$y = c + j \tag{5.14.5}$$

Income equals the sum of the production of consumption and investment goods.

5.15 The five equations determine the five variables c, j, w^{11}, w^{12}, and y for given values of the coefficients Λ^{11} or Λ^{12}.

The solution for j is obtained from the difference equation, which we find by substituting (5.14.4) in (5.14.2). The solution is

$$j_t = (1 + \Lambda^{11}\zeta^{11})^t j_0 \tag{5.15.1}$$

where j_0 is the investment volume in the initial period 0.

Similarly we find the solution for c by substituting (5.14.3) in (5.14.1), by using the solution for j_t and by solving the difference equation we find. The solution is

$$c_t = c_0 + \frac{\Lambda^{12}\zeta^{12}}{\Lambda^{11}\zeta^{11}}[(1 + \Lambda^{11}\zeta^{11})^t - 1]j_0 \tag{5.15.2}$$

By adding up the solutions for c and j, we find the solution for y:

$$y_t = y_0 + \left(1 + \frac{\Lambda^{12}\zeta^{12}}{\Lambda^{11}\zeta^{11}}\right)[(1 + \Lambda^{11}\zeta^{11})^t - 1]j_0 \tag{5.15.3}$$

5.16 The model does not introduce explicitly the rate of savings. However, this rate can be derived from the solutions for j and y. We find

$$\sigma_t = \frac{j_t}{y_t} = \frac{(1 + \Lambda^{11}\zeta^{11})^t j_0}{y_0 + (1 + \Lambda^{12}\zeta^{12}/\Lambda^{11}\zeta^{11})[(1 + \Lambda^{11}\zeta^{11})^t - 1]j_0} \tag{5.16.1}$$

This expression shows that σ is not constant, but changes over time with constant values of Λ^{11} and Λ^{12}. Thus, it appears that what seemed to be an additional degree of freedom—the possibility of substitution between the two capital goods—proves to be not a real one. We cannot choose independently the rate of savings and the allocation of investments between the two sectors at the same time (see Sec. 4.34).

Further analysis of Eq. (5.16.1) shows that, for constant values of Λ^{11} and Λ^{12}, the rate of savings increases and approaches asymptotically $\Lambda^{11}\zeta^{11}/(\Lambda^{11}\zeta^{11} + \Lambda^{12}\zeta^{12})$ for $t \to \infty$, if $\Lambda^{12}/\Lambda^{11} < w_0{}^{12}/w_0{}^{11}$ or $\Lambda^{12} < w_0{}^{12}/j_0$. Verbally, if the share of investment goods going into the consumer-goods industry is lower than this share in the initial period, the rate of savings increases. Similarly, we find that the rate of savings decreases and approaches the same asymptotical value for $t \to \infty$, if $\Lambda^{12}/\Lambda^{11} > w_0{}^{12}/w_0{}^{11}$ or $\Lambda^{12} > w_0{}^{12}/j_0$. The rate of savings remains constant only if the allocation of the investments between the two sectors is the same as in the initial period.

5.17 The use that can be made of this model for planning purposes is to choose the value of Λ^{12} (or Λ^{11}) so as to maximize the target variable of economic policy. Different targets can be considered, each leading to a different choice. The following cases may be mentioned.

1. To maximize y at a certain point of time T. As the solution we find that if T is below a certain value T_0, depending on the coefficients ζ, Λ^{12} should be equal to 1. If T is higher than another value T_1 (with $T_1 > T_0$), then Λ^{12} should be equal to zero. Only if T is in the range between the critical values T_0 and T_1, values of Λ^{12} (or Λ^{11}) between 1 and 0 are optimal. This range may be very small depending on the values for the ζ's.

This result can be understood if we deduce from Eq. (5.15.3) the value of the increase in y per time period at the time t:

$$\Delta y_t = (\Lambda^{11}\zeta^{11} + \Lambda^{12}\zeta^{12})(1 + \Lambda^{11}\zeta^{11})^t \mathfrak{y}_0$$

The second expression at the right-hand side increases with increasing values for Λ^{11}, while the first expression decreases, if $\zeta^{12} > \zeta^{11}$, which we normally can expect to be the case. For small values of t, the increase in the second term will be smaller than the decrease in the first term and, therefore, $\Lambda^{11} = 0$ (or $\Lambda^{12} = 1$) will lead to the highest increase.

2. To maximize c at a certain point of time T. Here also there exists a critical value T_0' below which $\Lambda^{12} = 1$ leads to a maximum value of c. However, there does not exist a second critical value T_1' above which Λ^{12} should be 0, for with $\Lambda^{12} = 0$, consumption remains constant.

5.18 Professor Mahalanobis has elaborated the two-sector model into a four-sector model by subdividing the consumer-goods industry in the following subsectors: factory production of consumer goods (sector 2), production of consumer goods (including agricultural products) in small and household industries (sector 3), and services, such as health and education (sector 4). Sector 1 indicates the investment-goods sector. In addition, the model introduces the labor requirements for each sector. The problem to be solved with the help of the model is again to determine the allocation of the investments over the four sectors.

The equations of the model are

$$\Delta a = \Delta a^1 + \Delta a^2 + \Delta a^3 + \Delta a^4 \qquad (5.18.1)$$

Total newly created employment (Δa) equals the sum of the new employment created in each sector separately (Δa^i).

$$\Lambda^i \mathfrak{j} = \Xi^i \, \Delta a^i \qquad i = 1, \ldots, 4 \qquad (5.18.2)$$

These equations introduce for each sector i a constant capital-labor ratio Ξ^i, the amount of net investment required for the employment of an additional worker. The equations relate the new investments in each sector to the new employment created. The Λ^i's have to fulfill the condition $\Sigma^i \Lambda^i = 1$.

$$\Delta y = j \cdot \sum_{1}^{4}{}^{i} \zeta^i \Lambda^i \qquad i = 1, \ldots, 4 \tag{5.18.3}$$

In this equation ζ^i is the output-capital ratio of sector i, and, consequently, $\Sigma \zeta^i \Lambda^i$ represents the weighted average of the output-capital ratios with the shares of each sector in total investments as weights.

The use which Mahalanobis has made of this model is, in our opinion, not the most appropriate. He deduces the value of Λ^1 from the two-sector model and fixes on a priori grounds the values for Δy, Δa, and j. In this case no real policy problem remains.

A more suitable use would be, for example, to give certain weights (ω_i) to an increase in employment and in income and to derive from the model the values for the Λ's which maximize the weighted sum $\omega_1 \Delta a + \omega_2 \Delta y$ over a given period. Alternative approaches are also possible.

5.2. Open-economy Models

5.21 We shall now take up again some open-economy models but, contrary to what was done in Sec. 4.4, introduce into them the element of substitution through international trade. We do this by making the choice of industries a major instrument of development policy. In the train of thought of the models here considered, the choice will depend above all on the comparative advantages a country may have in some industries and the comparative disadvantages in others. Maintaining the assumption of fixed and given prices of all products, we find that a comparative advantage will show itself in lower costs per unit of product. Costs in these examples are all inputs excluding inputs of factors of production, since their values are part of the national income, which we want to maximize.

5.22 The variables to be included in the models are

v^h production of good h
$v^{hh'}$ input of commodity h into current production of h'
$w^{hh'}$ input of commodity h into investments in sector h'
c^h consumption of good h
e^h export of good h (negative sign stands for imports)
y national income
s savings

5.23 The relations of the models are

$$w^{hh'} = \frac{\kappa^{hh'}}{\theta^{h'}} (v^{h'}_{t+\theta^{h'}} - v_t^{h'}) \tag{5.23.1}$$

$$s = \sum_h \sum_{h'} w^{hh'} \tag{5.23.2}$$

$$s = \sigma y \tag{5.23.3}$$

$$y = \sum_h \varphi^{0h} v^h \tag{5.23.4}$$

$$v^h = c^h + e^h + \sum_{h'} v^{hh'} + \sum_{h'} w^{hh'} \tag{5.23.5}$$

$$c^h = \gamma^h(y - s) + \bar{c}^h \tag{5.23.6}$$

$$v^{hh'} = \varphi^{hh'} v^{h'} \tag{5.23.7}$$

These relations do not need explanation, since they are identical with those of Sec. 4.6, except for the terms e^h, which, however, we met in Sec. 4.4.

5.24 As mentioned earlier, we are going to demonstrate the use of the model by solving the *second-stage planning problem of the choice of industries.* It is assumed again that a provisional choice of σ has been made and that at time $t = 0$ all $v_0{}^h$ are given: the economy simply uses to the full all production capacities it has inherited from the past. This means that y_0 as well as s_0 is also given.

Confining ourselves first to the case where again all $\theta^{h'}$ are equal and choosing $\theta^{h'} = \theta$, the solution of our problem consists in maximizing $y_{t+\theta}$ under the side condition that a given amount of investment is available, that is,

$$\sum_h \sum_{h'} w_0{}^{hh'} = \sum_h \sum_{h'} \frac{\kappa^{hh'}}{\theta} (v_\theta{}^{h'} - v_0{}^{h'}) = s_0 \tag{5.24.1}$$

Since the $v_0{}^{h'}$ are known, this side condition is a linear condition upon the $v_\theta{}^h$, whereas the maximand

$$y_\theta = \sum_h \varphi^{0h} v_\theta{}^h \tag{5.24.2}$$

is also linear in $v_\theta{}^h$. We must add, strictly speaking, some boundary conditions; to begin with

$$v_\theta{}^h > v_0{}^h \tag{5.24.3}$$

or, if capital goods are assumed to have a finite life, $v^h > v_0{}^h - d^h$, where d^h represents depreciation allowances in sector h; we shall neglect this detail, however.

There will be further boundary conditions which we will discuss later.

As the problem is now stated, each additional unit of s_0 devoted to investment into sector h' yields an addition to production $v^{h'}$ equal to

$$\frac{1}{\sum_h \kappa^{hh'}} = \frac{1}{\kappa^{h'}} \tag{5.24.4}$$

as can be read from Eq. (5.24.1); here $\kappa^{h'}$ is the capital-output ratio of sector h'. The contribution to national income in year θ is, according to (5.24.2),

$$\frac{\varphi^{0h'}}{\kappa^{h'}} \tag{5.24.5}$$

As a rule, these figures will be different for the various sectors. In order to get the maximum value of y_θ, all investment should therefore be directed to sector h^m, showing the maximum value of (5.24.5). If, by coincidence, two sectors had the same, highest, figure, it would not matter which sector was chosen. After the $v_\theta{}^h$ had been chosen, the equations of Sec. 5.23 would enable the planning authority to determine the unknowns for year 0, that is, $w_0{}^{hh'}$, $e_0{}^h$, which can be found from Eqs. (5.23.1) and (5.23.5).

5.25 Some comments on the economic significance of the procedure just described are called for.

1. The assumption that σ has already been determined on the basis of a macromodel implies some general *knowledge about export possibilities*, for example, in the form suggested in Sec. 4.4. If this knowledge were exact, the values fcund for $e_0{}^h$ should be in conformity with it. In the absence of such conformity, there may be scope for revising the original assumptions, which may influence the value to be given to σ.

2. The device obtained from the maximization of y_θ is, in the language of the theory of international trade, one of *complete specialization*. Had such a device been followed in the past also, the country would produce one commodity only and import all others. The device is clearly unrealistic. It is based on the same two assumptions on which the simpler theories of international trade are based: (a) absence of transportation costs and (b) smallness of the country's supply in relation to the world market; otherwise the price cannot be considered fixed and given. A more realistic approach can be obtained by the following additional assumptions.

a. Some sectors may show very high transportation costs, making it impossible to have any international trade, whether exports or imports, meaning that $e_t{}^h = 0$ for $t = \theta$ as well as for $t = 0$.[1]

[1] This assumption has an implication for the choice of industries which deserves some further elaboration. It implies that there is no point in isolated investment

b. There may be boundary conditions set to the quantities $v_\theta{}^h$ which can be sold at the given price levels. This implies that the sector showing maximum (5.24.5) must have a v^h equal to this boundary value; if not all savings are needed for the corresponding investment, the next highest value of (5.24.5) will indicate a second sector to invest in, and so on.

These boundary conditions, though they make the model much more realistic, are, at the same time, its weakness: they have to be arbitrary. It makes much more sense here to introduce either nonlinear cost functions or a quantity-price relationship implying that larger quantities can be sold only at a lower price. Nonlinear cost functions will be taken up in Secs. 5.4 to 5.6. Quantity-price relationships will be taken up in Chap. 6.

5.26 A few remarks should be added about the case of *nonuniform gestation periods.* As in Sec. 4.7, we shall treat this case by considering a simple concrete model with two sectors, showing two different *lags* taken here to be $\theta^1 = 2$ and $\theta^2 = 3$ years. For practical purposes the lags can always be assumed to be commensurate. Considering the expressions, in terms of v's, for income in years 2 and 3, we have

$$y_2 = \underline{\varphi^{01}v_2{}^1} + \varphi^{02}v_2{}^2 \tag{5.26.1}$$

$$y_3 = \varphi^{01}v_3{}^1 + \underline{\varphi^{02}v_3{}^2} \tag{5.26.2}$$

With the aid of our savings s_0 we can contribute to $v_2{}^1$ and $v_3{}^2$, the underlined terms; decisions on $v_2{}^2$ have already been taken before (at time -1, since $\theta^2 = 3$), whereas decisions with regard to $v_3{}^1$ have to be

---

projects in any single sector; a project should always include a number of complementary investments in the sectors with very high transportation costs (the so-called national sectors; see Sec. 1.52). The size of the necessary complementary investments may be estimated with the aid of our models, that is, with input-output models, by the following set of equations:

$\Delta v^h = \Delta e^h + \sum_{h'} \varphi^{hh'} \, \Delta v^{h'}$ for all sectors

$\Delta v^h = 1/\kappa^h$ for original sector of project

$\Delta e^h = 0$ for complementary (national) sectors

$\Delta v^h = 0$ for international sectors other than original project sector

Terms Δc^h and $\sum_{h'} \Delta w^{hh'}$ have been omitted from Eq. (5.23.5) since no change in consumption or investment is assumed for the purpose of the present problem. The only question concerning us here is the necessary additional production in the national sectors needed in order that all interindustry deliveries are available. This is a first approximation. A more elaborate system may be set up in order to take into account the increase in consumption made possible by the increase in national income as a consequence of the project.

taken later (at time +1). In these circumstances it seems reasonable to *maximize* $\varphi^{01}v_2^1 + \varphi^{02}v_3^2$, that is, *the contributions to future income which can be made out of savings* s_0. This principle accepted, the procedure is practically identical to the one outlined in Sec. 5.24.

5.27 The reader should be reminded of what was said in Chap. 1 and in Sec. 3.5 about the role of aims in the design of economic policy. Clearly it is possible to use our models for the solution of planning problems with aims different from those assumed in the preceding sections.

5.3. Models with a Structural Break

5.31 It is essential for the process of industrialization that, from time to time, new sectors be added to the economy. In the language used in this book it is better to say that an "empty sector" becomes a normal sector. In fact, even if in the economy studied there is no production of a certain commodity, the sector has to be included in our model, showing consumption, interindustry deliveries, and imports of that commodity. What changes therefore is only the side condition $v^h = 0$ characteristic of the sector's "emptiness." This change constitutes, however, a change in the logical structure of a model, to which it is useful to give some attention.

5.32 The reasons for such a break to occur may be, on the one hand, changes in the price or cost data or in the boundaries introduced in Sec. 5.25 or, on the other hand, changes in the size of demand inside the country. As we saw in our models of Chaps. 4 and 5, changes in prices or costs will translate themselves into changes in φ^{0h}, and these can influence the choice of industries. The same is true of changes in boundary conditions. If the break occurs for one of these reasons, the procedure discussed will automatically result in a change in the production pattern.

A change in the size of home demand may be another reason, in practice, for starting home production. Economies of scale will often be involved. The models so far presented do not show this feature, since, mathematically speaking, it introduces nonlinear relationships which it is much more difficult to handle, especially if a large number of variables are involved. Again it may be helpful to proceed in stages and to use "partial models" in order to decide whether production of a certain commodity should be started. This decision taken, our linear models may again be used to study the consequences for the economy as a whole. We shall deal with some examples of this partial nonlinear research in Sec. 5.6.

5.33 The development of an economy introducing a new item to its production program passes through *three stages.* In the first stage, production is zero and investment in the sector is zero too. In the second stage, preparations for future production must be taken in the form of investments, which are positive now, while production is still zero. In the third stage, finally, production will be positive. In our symbols, we have

Stage I: $v_t^h = v_{t+\theta}^h = 0$
Stage II: $v_t^h = 0 \qquad v_{t+\theta}^h > 0$
Stage III: $v_t^h > 0 \qquad v_{t+\theta}^h > 0$

Clearly the length of stage II is θ, or rather θ^h.

5.34 In principle, the general mathematical solutions presented in Secs. 4.2, 4.4, 4.6, etc., are valid only for periods without a structural break. From the moment of a structural break, the path of development may change and has to be calculated anew.

5.4. Models with Increasing Marginal Costs

5.41 So far it has been assumed that production has taken place under conditions of constant returns, implying constant marginal costs equal to average costs. This assumption, usual in input-output analysis, has been responsible for the result indicating that complete specialization should be aimed at in order to maximize national product. In various situations this is an unrealistic assumption. We shall now consider alternative assumptions. They can be labeled by the well-known concepts of increasing marginal costs (or diminishing returns) and decreasing marginal costs (or increasing returns). The former phenomenon is characteristic of any given enterprise when capacity limits are approached and of some industries as a whole, especially agriculture and mining. The latter phenomenon is characteristic of enterprises or industries using *indivisible factors of production* and showing overcapacity. The phenomenon of increasing marginal costs is compatible with the assumption of free competition and can be dealt with analytically in a rather simple way. The phenomenon of decreasing marginal costs, or of indivisibilities, is incompatible with free competition in that it creates, at least if flat-rate pricing is applied, permanent losses to the competitors. There are therefore complications of a particular type; we shall deal with some of these later (see Secs. 5.5 and 5.6).

5.42 If in some sectors increasing marginal costs prevail, relations (5.23.7), for these sectors, will have to be replaced by nonlinear relationships. A simple example is a quadratic relationship.

$$v^{hh'} = \varphi_1{}^{hh'}v^{h'} + \tfrac{1}{2}\varphi_2{}^{hh'}(v^{h'})^2 \tag{5.42.1}$$

Such relationships may facilitate the solution of our maximum problem. Income y is no longer a linear function of all v^h, but a quadratic function of some v^h. This means that the expression $\varphi^{0h'}/\kappa^{h'}$ has to be replaced by a more complicated one, depending on $v^{h'}$, and that a maximum y may be found for finite values of the $v^{h'}$, characterized by equal marginal income-capital ratios. In the case where all sectors showed rather rapidly increasing marginal costs, this maximum would be represented by

$$\frac{\partial y_\theta}{\partial v_\theta{}^h} + \Psi \frac{\partial s_0}{\partial v_\theta{}^h} = 0 \qquad h = 1, \ldots, H \tag{5.42.2}$$

where Ψ is a Lagrangian multiplier and where

$$\frac{\partial y_\theta}{\partial v_\theta{}^h} = \varphi^{0h} - v_\theta{}^h \sum_{h'} \varphi_2{}^{h'h} \qquad \varphi^{0h} = 1 - \sum_{h'} \varphi_1{}^{h'h} \tag{5.42.3}$$

whereas, as before, $\partial s_0/\partial v_\theta{}^h = \kappa^h/\theta$, leading to

$$\frac{\varphi^{01} - v_\theta{}^1 \sum_{h'} \varphi_2{}^{h'1}}{\kappa^1} = \frac{\varphi^{02} - v_\theta{}^2 \sum_{h'} \varphi_2{}^{h'2}}{\kappa^2} = \cdots = \frac{\varphi^{0H} - v_\theta{}^H \sum_{h'} \varphi_2{}^{h'H}}{\kappa^H} \tag{5.42.4}$$

This solution will only apply, however, if all sectors but one show increasing costs, and if the values found satisfy the boundary conditions $v_\theta{}^h \geq v_0{}^h$. Otherwise, a number of $v_\theta{}^h$ will have to be put equal to $v_0{}^h$, while the others satisfy conditions of the nature of (5.42.4).

5.5. Indivisibilities

5.51 It is well known that indivisibilities play a role in the process of development, that is, the fact that some investment projects make sense only when they have a certain minimum size. This is true for railways, because at least one track has to be constructed over the whole distance between two centers before transportation can take place at all. It is true for almost any project in some sense. In order to be an economic proposition a factory has to have a certain minimum size before all types of overhead expenses are justified. A university with a few hundreds of students only would not provide a full-time job to most of the teaching staff, and so on.

When it comes to expressing this well-known truth in terms of development models, it must be stated that very little is known quantitatively about the precise role indivisibilities play. There are no very clear macroeconomic observations which can be explained only by the phenomenon of indivisibilities. Although one can easily imagine all sorts of impacts of them on macroeconomic development, there are all sorts of "escapes" to indivisibilities too. It is true that any single railway constitutes an example, but the number of railway connections in most countries is so large that the construction of the railway network can be and actually has been spread over a long period in most countries, and the investment involved in each single year need not be a very large portion of total investment. Even if the construction of an irrigation dam for a small region is very much an indivisibility, for a country as a whole such projects need not coincide and do not therefore take such a large portion of investment resources. Often also the long construction period helps to spread the effects. Although it cannot be denied that the Aswan High Dam in Egypt will absorb a considerable portion of the country's investment resources, to quote a recent example, it is hardly possible to say that indivisibilities play a standard role in the development of every country which can be represented by some standard feature in models for development planning. The most natural way to deal with the problem is to admit that among the projects which together constitute the investment program of a country there may be some whose size is considerable, and that in appraising them the consequences for the economy as a whole should be carefully considered. In the subsections of this section, a model for the appraisal of projects will be shown in which the size of the projects is considered given and may be large. The choice of the size of some types of projects in which indivisibilities play a role is treated in Sec. 5.6.

5.52 The model for the *appraisal of investment projects*, which is explained in the following subsections, assumes that a number of big and indivisible projects is given from which a selection has to be made. The model helps to estimate the impact of a given investment program on the national product and its development over time. The model assumes an open economy and two scarce factors of production: capital and foreign exchange.

Two groups of economic variables are distinguished: those which apply to the projects and those which do not. The project variables are indicated by an upper index h, where $h = 1, 2, \ldots, H$, if H is the total number of available projects from which the selection has to be made. Each index corresponds to an investment project. A combination of projects is called an investment program, and the total of all h-variables the program sector. Variables with an upper index 0 apply to variables outside the program sector, to be called the rest of the economy. Variables which are a combination of 0- and h-variables do not carry an index.

5.53 The following variables are used in the model, leaving out the upper indices.

Y	net national product (or income)
v	volume of gross product
S	value of savings
c	volume of consumption expenditure
k	real capital stock in use
e	volume of exports
i	volume of imports
F	balance-of-payments deficit
M^h	foreign debt incurred for the execution of project h
m^i	interest rate for foreign debts
$\bar{m}$	rate of discount
p	price level of national product
p^i	price level of imports

5.54 The equations of the model are

$$Y^0 = v^0 p - i^0 p^i - \delta k^0 p \tag{5.54.1}$$
$$Y^h = v^h p - i^h p^i - \delta k^h p - m^i M^h \tag{5.54.2}$$

These equations define in the usual way the contribution of the rest of the economy and of each project to national income. Vertical integration is assumed within the rest of the economy and within each project. The term $m^i M^h$ in (.2) represents the interest paid on the foreign debt incurred for project h. The coefficient δ represents the rate of depreciation on the capital stock in use. This coefficient is assumed to be the same in both sectors.

$$Y^0 = c^0 p + \dot{k}^0 p + e^0 p - i^0 p^i \tag{5.54.3}$$
$$Y^h = c^h p + \dot{k}^h p + e^h p - i^h p^i - m^i M^h \tag{5.54.4}$$

These equations define the contribution to national income from the expenditure side. They have the function to determine, in combination with other equations, the export volumes. The terms $\dot{k}^0 p$ and $\dot{k}^h p$ represent the net investment in the rest of the economy and in project h, respectively.

$$c^0 p = \gamma^0 (Y^0 + \Sigma Y^h) + \bar{c}^0 p \tag{5.54.5}$$
$$c^h p = \gamma^h (Y^0 + \Sigma Y^h) + \bar{c}^h p \tag{5.54.6}$$
$$i^0 = \iota^0 v^0 \tag{5.54.7}$$
$$i^h = \iota^h v^h \tag{5.54.8}$$
$$S^0 = \sigma^0 Y^0 \tag{5.54.9}$$
$$S^h = \sigma^h Y^h \tag{5.54.10}$$
$$S = S^0 + \Sigma S^h \tag{5.54.11}$$

The equations (.9) and (.10) formulate an essential feature of the model. They express the assumption that each project has its own rate of savings. Differences in the rate of savings between projects may be the consequence of differences in the distribution of the income generated by each project. Especially the distribution in labor and nonlabor income will be relevant. Roughly speaking, this distribution is correlated to the labor or capital intensity of the project.

$$\kappa^0 v^0 = k^0 \tag{5.54.12}$$

$$\kappa^h v^h = k^h \tag{5.54.13}$$

$$\dot{M}^h = p^i i^h - \frac{1}{\tau} M^h \tag{5.54.14}$$

This equation indicates the net capital imports on account of project h. It is assumed that during the construction period, capital is imported equal to the value of the imports of capital goods (I^h) needed for project h. During the operation period the loan (M^h) is repaid at an annual rate of $(1/\tau)M^h$ if τ is the period of repayment.

$$p(\dot{k}^0 + \Sigma\dot{k}^h) = S + F + \Sigma\dot{M}^h - \delta(k^0 + \Sigma k^h)p \tag{5.54.15}$$

This is a balance equation for capital formation. The left-hand side of the equation indicates the value of net capital investments, the right-hand side the available sources to finance these investments. The balance-of-payments deficit F is defined in the following equation:

$$F = p^i(i^0 + \Sigma i^h) - p(e^0 + \Sigma e^h) + m^i\Sigma M^h - \Sigma\dot{M}^h \tag{5.54.16}$$

The deficit F is not the deficit on current account, but on current and capital account to the extent that the capital items have a planned character.

5.55 The following variables are explained by the model: Y^0, v^0, c^0, e^0, i^0, S^0, k^0, Y^h, v^h, c^h, e^h, i^h, S^h, $\dot{M}^h$, S, and F. These $9 + 7\,H$-variables are equal in number to the number of equations. The investments k^h made for each project and the prices p^i, p, and m^i are assumed to be given.

The economic structure of the model may be explained as follows. The existing capital stock and the additions to it determine the level of gross production and the direct contribution of each project to national income. Each project generates savings which become available for financing the investments in the rest of the economy in addition to its own savings and make possible a further increase in production and income. This shows that, according to the model, an investment program influences total national income not only directly but also indirectly via the influence on total savings.

The model enables us to determine the development of total national income $(Y^0 + \Sigma Y^h)$ over time for any given investment program.

Different programs may lead to different development patterns. In order to be able to choose between alternative programs, a criterion is needed which summarizes the development patterns. As such a criterion, we could choose the discounted value of the future total national product $\bar{Y}_1$.

$$\bar{Y}_1 = \sum_{1}^{\infty}{}^{t} \frac{Y_t^0 + \Sigma Y_t^h}{\prod_{2}^{t} (1 + \bar{m}_{t'})}$$

The rate of discount $\bar{m}$ is made variable but may also be a constant.[1] If the total volume of the investment program is given, the selection of the projects to be included in the program has to be made in such a way as to maximize $\bar{Y}_1$. This combination of projects can be found only by trial and error.

5.6. Nonlinear Partial Models

5.61 Indivisibilities play their role at an innumerable number of spots in any economy. In a single factory, each machine is an example, and examples can be found all the way up to the really giant projects that sometimes must be part of a development process. For the economist engaged in macroplanning, it is not usually feasible to go into all the details of these indivisibilities. Looked at in a more comprehensive way, they show themselves in the nonlinear shape of some cost functions. Plotting total costs against the volume of production of a factory, we shall often find that they must be represented by a curve rather than a straight line. Depending on the form of the cost curve, there may or may not be some optimum size of the factory or of any other investment project, a phenomenon of considerable importance for development programming. Thus, a new industry should not be started as a rule if the market for its product does not permit a size of the factory in the neighborhood of the optimum size.

Though theoretically attractive, it would be practically impossible to introduce curvilinear cost functions as a regular feature for most sectors in a development model. Mathematical, and even numerical, treatment of such functions soon becomes impossible if their numbers increase. This is another reason for applying the device of planning in stages and for singling out the problems of deciding about the size of single plants or projects from the general programming problem by first considering a

[1] Here $\prod_{2}^{t} (1 + \bar{m}_{t'})$ stands for $(1 + \bar{m}_2)(1 + \bar{m}_3) \cdots (1 + \bar{m}_t)$.

partial problem, when necessary with the aid of a partial model. The justification to do so is that in many cases the dimensions of single projects are small in comparison with the economy as a whole and that therefore variations in the size of such projects do not affect the market and other variables of the economy as a whole. Therefore the latter can be treated as given and the partial problem solved without considering all the interconnections of the economy. We shall give some examples of this type of partial research in the subsequent subsections.

5.62 As already explained, the many almost hidden indivisibilities playing roles in any single factory may give rise to a cost function of a curvilinear nature, as shown in the textbooks on business economics. Let total costs be a quadratic function of production v, for example,

$$\psi_0 + \psi_1 v + \psi_2 v^2$$

Then unit costs will be a minimum for

$$\frac{d}{dv}\left(\frac{\psi_0}{v} + \psi_1 + \psi_2 v\right) = 0$$

or

$$-\frac{\psi_0}{v^2} + \psi_2 = 0$$

or $v = \sqrt{\psi_0/\psi_2}$, representing the optimum size of the enterprise.

5.63 In some cases, transportation costs may be a decisive element in finding the optimum size of an enterprise. The larger the volume of production, the longer the average distance over which the product must be transported in order to reach the customer. Let demand be proportional to the surface over which the commodity can be supplied; if it is supplied over a circle with radius ρ, the average distance as well as the marginal one is proportional to ρ. Since the total quantity demanded varies with the surface of the circle, which is $\pi\rho^2$, the radius of the circle is proportional to $\sqrt{v}$. So are transportation costs per unit. If production costs proper are of the usual linear type $\psi_0 + \psi_1 v$, total costs, including transportation, are of the shape $\psi_0 + \psi_1 v + \psi_2 v\sqrt{v}$. Unit costs will then be $\psi_0/v + \psi_1 + \psi_2\sqrt{v}$, and these again will be a minimum if

$$-\frac{\psi_0}{v^2} + \frac{1}{2}\frac{\psi_2}{\sqrt{v}} = 0$$

or

$$v = \left(\frac{2\psi_0}{\psi_2}\right)^{2/3}$$

5.64 Frequently labor productivity in the initial stages of a new enterprise, especially in underdeveloped countries, will be too low to permit the enterprise to compete in the world market. At short notice it will then be more advantageous for the country to import the commodity considered—apart from questions of employment or balance of payments. Since it is a common experience, however, that after some years of exercise, productivity increases, a partial study may be made about the prospects at somewhat longer notice; it may well be that the enterprise turns out to be competitive in the long run. On such evidence the decision may be taken to establish the unit.

Among the appropriate subjects for partial studies market analyses for export products should be mentioned also. Such analyses may include an exploration into the factors determining the size of the market, such as incomes in customer countries, size of competing crops, price level at which the commodity is sold, changes in commercial or fiscal policy of the customer countries or the producing country, and so on. As far as possible the quantitative influence of such factors should also be determined. Since econometric studies of this kind are the subject of many publications and textbooks, the reader may be referred to such sources.

Chapter 6

SEVERAL SECTORS; VARIABLE PRICES

6.1. Two-sector Model for Terms of Trade

6.11 In this chapter, models will be discussed in which prices are among the variables to be planned. In Chap. 1 we discussed the necessity to do so in a number of cases. These cases will now be taken up.

In Sec. 2.14, the Harrod-Domar model was adapted to an open economy. However, no prices were introduced, implying the assumption that exports are salable at the constant price level assumed. We shall now assume that exports can be increased only at a lowering of export prices. This will be the case, for example, for the underdeveloped countries which are the main suppliers on one of the world commodity markets. Imports, in this case mainly consisting of capital and other finished goods, are assumed to be dependent on the national product. Interindustry deliveries are neglected, and two sectors are distinguished: the country concerned and the rest of the world. The price level introduced in the model represents the terms of trade of the country with the rest of the world.[1]

The planning problems that can be studied with the help of this model are, for example, the rate of growth of the national income which leads to balance-of-payments equilibrium and full utilization of the capital supplied and the rate of savings which maximizes the national income at a certain future point of time.

6.12 The variables used are

k volume of capital

v gross national product

c consumption

[1] See P. J. Verdoorn, Complementarity and Long-range Projections, *Econometrica*, vol. 24, no. 4, p. 429, 1956.

e volume of exports
i volume of imports
y real national income
p terms of trade of country with rest of the world

6.13 The equations of the model are

$$k = \kappa v \quad (6.13.1)$$
$$\dot{k} = \sigma y \quad (6.13.2)$$
$$v = c + \dot{k} + e - i \quad (6.13.3)$$
$$y = c + \dot{k} + ep - i \quad (6.13.4)$$

As a consequence of changes in the terms of trade, we have to distinguish between the volume of output measured by v and the real national product y. The import price level is used as *numéraire.*

$$i = \iota v \quad (6.13.5)$$
$$e = e(p) \quad (6.13.6')$$

or more specifically

$$e = e_0 p^\epsilon \quad (6.13.6)$$

where e_0 is a constant and ϵ the (constant) price elasticity.

$$ep = i \quad (6.13.7)$$

This equation formulates the condition of equilibrium in the balance of payments.

6.14 The seven equations of the model are just sufficient to determine the seven variables. For example, the solution for the terms of trade p is

$$p_t = \left(p_0 - \frac{\iota}{1+\iota}\right) e^{\frac{\sigma}{\kappa}\frac{1+\iota}{1+\epsilon}t} + \frac{\iota}{1+\iota} \quad (6.14.1)$$

From this equation it follows that the terms of trade improve if $-1 < \epsilon < 0$, and deteriorate if $\epsilon < -1$.

If we want to determine the rate of savings which maximizes y at the point of time t, we first derive the solution for y, differentiate y with regard to σ, and put $dy/d\sigma$ equal to zero. We find that

$$\frac{\epsilon}{1+\epsilon}\frac{\iota}{1+\iota} = \left(p_0 - \frac{\iota}{1+\iota}\right) e^{\frac{\sigma}{\kappa}\frac{1+\iota}{1+\epsilon}t} + \frac{\iota}{1+\iota} \quad (6.14.2)$$

This expression enables us to determine the value of σ which maximizes y at any point of time t. The expression shows that σ has to vary inversely proportional to t. The relationship between σ and the coefficients ϵ and ι appears to be fairly complicated.

6.2. Open Economy Input-Output Model with World-demand Equations

6.21 We are now going to take up again the multisector input-output model, which we discussed in Sec. 5.2, dropping the assumption of constant prices in order to express the influence that changes in production volumes may exert on prices and hence on national income. This means that we are giving a more flexible significance to the concept of (comparative) advantages to be derived from international trade.

6.22 The variables of the model are

v^h production of good h
$v^{hh'}$ input of commodity h into current production of h'
$w^{hh'}$ input of commodity h into investments in sector h'
c^h consumption of good h
e^h exports (with negative sign: imports) of good h
p^h price level of commodity h
Y national income (in money terms)
S savings (in money terms)

6.23 The relations of the model are

$$w^{hh'} = \frac{\kappa^{hh'}}{\theta}(v^{h'}_{t+\theta} - v^{h'}) \tag{6.23.1}$$

$$S = \sum_h \sum_{h'} w^{hh'} p^h \tag{6.23.2}$$

$$S = \sigma Y \tag{6.23.3}$$

$$Y = \sum_h v^h p^h - \sum_h \sum_{h'} v^{hh'} p^h \tag{6.23.4}$$

$$v^h = c^h + e^h + \sum_{h'} v^{hh'} + \sum_{h'} w^{hh'} \tag{6.23.5}$$

$$c^h p^h = \gamma^h (Y - S) + \Sigma \gamma^{hh'} p^{h'} + \bar{c}^h \bar{p} \tag{6.23.6}$$

As before, we assume that $\Sigma\gamma^h = 1$, $\Sigma\bar{c}^h = 0$, and all $c^h \geq 0$; in addition we now assume that, for all values of h', $\sum_h \gamma^{hh'} = 0$. The consequence of these assumptions again will be that $\Sigma c^h p^h = Y - S$.

$$v^{hh'} = \varphi^{hh'} v^{h'} \tag{6.23.7}$$

$$p^h = \pi^h(v^h) \tag{6.23.8}$$

These equations express the relationship between p^h and v^h as a consequence of world demand. Other variables may occur in the relationship π^h, but it is assumed that these are exogenous variables, which can be considered given. Some more general assumptions will be discussed in Sec. 6.4.

6.24 The use of this model will be illustrated again by considering the second stage of a planning problem arising after the rate of savings has been chosen. As in Sec. 5.24, we assume that all $v_0{}^h$ are given as a consequence of previous investments, and that the problem of choosing the production pattern for time period θ is considered. Again we assume that a maximization of income is aimed at under the side condition of given savings. It is possible, with the aid of relations (6.237) and (6.238), to write Y as a function of v^h only and to apply this formula to year θ.

$$Y_\theta = \sum_h \Big(v_\theta{}^h - \sum_{h'} \varphi^{hh'} v_\theta{}^{h'}\Big)\pi^h(v_\theta{}^h) \tag{6.24.1}$$

Also savings S_0 can be expressed in terms of $v_\theta{}^h$:

$$S_0 = \sum_h \sum_{h'} \frac{\kappa^{hh'}}{\theta}(v_\theta{}^{h'} - v_0{}^{h'})p_0{}^h \tag{6.24.2}$$

which is a linear function in $v_\theta{}^h$. Our problem will then be to maximize (6.24.1) under the side condition (6.24.2). The solution can be written with the aid of a Lagrangian multiplier Ψ.

$$\frac{\partial Y_\theta}{\partial v_\theta} + \Psi \frac{\partial S_0}{\partial v_\theta} = 0 \tag{6.24.3}$$

or

$$\pi^h(v_\theta{}^h) + v_\theta{}^h \frac{d\pi^h}{dv_\theta{}^h} - \frac{d\pi^h}{dv_\theta{}^h} \sum_{h'} \varphi^{hh'} v_\theta{}^{h'} - \sum_{h'} \varphi^{hh'} \pi^{h'}(v_\theta{}^{h'}) + \Psi \sum_{h'} \frac{\kappa^{h'h}}{\theta} p_0{}^{h'} = 0 \tag{6.24.4}$$

In this problem as well as in that of Sec. 5.24 some boundary conditions will have to be respected; again all $v_\theta{}^h - v_0{}^h$ should be positive (or not surpass, when negative, the absolute figure of depreciation allowances). It will depend very much on the nature of the functions π^h whether such boundary conditions rather than the maximum conditions (6.24.4) will become active.

6.3. Nonlinear Cost Functions

6.31 The model just described can be further adapted to reality, for the sectors where this is essential, by the introduction of nonlinear cost functions. As already observed, agriculture and mining may operate under increasing marginal costs, and this phenomenon can be taken account of rather easily, as shown in Sec. 5.4. In somewhat loose nonmathematical terms, there are two reasons why increased production in a sector may make its contribution, per unit of capital invested, to future national income less than in the initial situation: increasing costs and decreasing prices. If the sectors contributing most, per unit of invested capital, to national income are of one of these two types, their marginal contribution will be reduced with increasing production, and the optimum will be characterized by marginal contributions which are equal for all sectors in which investment is planned.

6.32 The situation is less simple for sectors working under decreasing marginal costs, which as a rule are the expression of the existence of indivisibilities of some kind. As already indicated in Chap. 5, the problem of finding the optimum program then can best be solved by making use of partial models, going into details it would be difficult to introduce in a general way for all sectors.

6.4. Other Demand Functions

Another adaptation to reality of the model discussed in Sec. 6.2 is to introduce other demand functions.

In the model of Sec. 6.2, the price in each sector was assumed to be a function of gross output in that sector: $p^h = \pi^h(v^h)$. This demand equation, which, however, could also be interpreted as a cost function, is based on the assumption that the internal prices adapt themselves to the corresponding foreign prices and that these prices determine the demand for both home and foreign demand, for final consumption, and other uses.

A more complicated situation arises when uniform domestic and foreign prices can no longer be assumed. Here, for example, separate demand functions for home and foreign demand may be necessary. Foreign demand could then depend on the (relative) price difference at home and abroad.

A further refinement could be to introduce the substitutability or complementarity in the demand equations by making p^h a function not only of v^h but also of the gross output in one or more other sectors h'.

Generally, to introduce these refinements in the models would very soon lead to unmanageable results. Here also partial methods could be linked to the over-all planning models.

6.5. Alternative Techniques: A Linear Programming Model

6.51 In this section we shall discuss an example of the use of the linear programming technique in formulating a development model.[1]

Mathematically, a linear programming model is bound to linear equations, which implies in many cases a serious limitation on the number of development problems to which such a model could be applied, or a distortion of reality if the assumption of linearity is made without good reasons. The dynamic nature of nearly all planning models is another difficulty.

[1] For a general exposition of the mathematical and economic aspects of linear programming, see, for example, R. Dorfman, P. A. Samuelson, and R. Solow, "Linear Programming and Economic Analysis," New York, 1958.

The following section describes an interesting attempt by Mr. J. Sandee to develop a planning model for India using linear programming technique.[1] The model takes the situation in 1960 as its starting point and tries to determine an optimum situation for 1970. Our description is formulated in general terms and, therefore, is independent of Mr. Sandee's statistical application to the case of India. Our formulation makes possible comparison with the other models in this book.

6.52 The variables of the model are

v^h production of good h
$v^{hh'}$ input of commodity h into current production of h'
$w^{hh'}$ input of commodity h into investments in sector h'
j total volume of investment
c^h consumption of good h
c total volume of consumption
e^h exports (imports with negative sign) of good h
y real national product

All variables measure differences between the variables at the end and at the beginning of the planning period.

6.53 The equations of the model are the following:

$$w^{hh'} = \frac{2}{T}\kappa^{hh'}v^{h'} - 2w_0{}^{hh'} \qquad (6.53.1)$$

The assumption is made that all investments increase (or decrease) linearly with time during the planning period. If the planning period is T years, and if $w_0{}^{hh'}$ represents the investment flow of commodity h into sector h' in the year before the first year of the planning period, then the flow of investment in the last year of the planning period is equal to $w_0{}^{hh'} + w^{hh'}$. Total investment during this period is $T(w_0{}^{hh'} + \frac{1}{2}w^{hh'})$, which can be related to the increase in gross output of sector h'.

$$T(w_0{}^{hh'} + \tfrac{1}{2}w^{hh'}) = \kappa^{hh'}v^{h'}$$

or

$$w^{hh'} = \frac{2}{T}\kappa^{hh'}v^{h'} - 2w_0{}^{hh'}$$

$$j = \Sigma\Sigma w^{hh'} \qquad (6.53.2)$$

$$v^h = c^h + e^h + \Sigma v^{hh'} + \Sigma w^{hh'} \qquad (6.53.3)$$

$$c = \Sigma c^h \qquad (6.53.4)$$

$$v^{hh'} = \varphi^{hh'}v^{h'} \qquad (6.53.5)$$

$$\Sigma e^h = 0 \qquad (6.53.6)$$

[1] J. Sandee, "A Demonstration Planning Model for India," Calcutta, 1960.

This equation defines the condition that no changes in the balance-of-payments situation will take place. Imports are considered as negative exports.

$$\bar{e}^h < e^h < \bar{\bar{e}}^h \tag{6.53.7}$$

$$\bar{w}^{hh'} < w^{hh'} < \bar{\bar{w}}^{hh'} \tag{6.53.8}$$

$$\bar{c}^h < c^h < \bar{\bar{c}}^h \tag{6.53.9}$$

The inequalities (.7), (.8), and (.9) are boundary conditions set on the variables e^h, $w^{hh'}$, and c^h. Both the lower bounds $\bar{e}^h$, $\bar{w}^{hh'}$, and $\bar{c}^h$ as well as the upper bounds $\bar{\bar{e}}^h$, $\bar{\bar{w}}^{hh'}$, and $\bar{\bar{c}}^h$ are determined on *ad hoc* reasonings. The inequalities (.7) and (.9) are substitutes for the export demand and consumption equations.

$$j \leq \frac{\sigma}{1-\sigma} c \tag{6.53.10}$$

This inequality sets an upper limit on total investment. A marginal propensity to save equal to σ implies that per unit increase of income σ is invested and $1 - \sigma$ consumed, or per unit increase in consumption investment rises $\sigma/(1 - \sigma)$. The propensity to save is assumed to be constant.

Subject to the above equations and inequalities, total consumption c as a target can be maximized and the allocation of total investment determined.

Chapter 7

SEVERAL SECTORS AND SEVERAL REGIONS

7.1. Rigid Distribution of Inputs over Sectors of Origin

7.11 In the present chapter, models are discussed in which the economy is subdivided not only according to sectors but also according to geography. The geographical units will be called regions; they are parts of a country.[1] Regions will be indicated by prefixes (indexes placed in front of the main symbol) r, the total number of regions being R. Models of this type make it possible to consider problems of development policy and planning in which targets are set referring either to the relative position of the regions or to particular regions.

The subdivision of the economy into regions forces us to consider a number of phenomena which we need not discuss when we use models without a geographical subdivision, phenomena which are familiar to the student of international economic problems. B. Ohlin[2] has already pointed out many of the parallels and some differences between international and interregional economic intercourse.

A geographical subdivision of the economy introduces movements between regions, of both products and factors of production. In both categories we meet cases of high and of low mobility, and we have a choice between crude and more detailed approaches to these phenomena. The crudest, but often quite useful, approach is to distinguish between products or factors which cannot move on the one hand and which move freely on the other hand. Free movements will be present if no cost of transportation occurs. The crudest approach means that there are either

[1] The word "region" is also used for areas larger than countries; this meaning will, however, not be given to the word in this book.

[2] B. Ohlin, "Interregional and International Trade," p. 45, Cambridge, Mass., 1933.

prohibitive or no costs of transportation. We shall call those sectors the products of which cannot move outside the region *regional sectors;* sectors the products of which cannot move outside the economy, *national sectors.*

Of the factor movements, capital movements are the most important to us, since we assume that capital is a scarce factor. Population and labor movements, as long as this factor is abundant, are irrelevant to the economy. In reality they are not, of course; the simplest way of dealing with this phenomenon is to admit that population movements are creating boundary conditions to the production capacity of sectors, to the extent that labor, or certain types of labor, becomes scarce. In an economy where labor is scarce generally, labor movements will have to be treated with the same degree of precision as capital movements.

In a more refined approach, we shall deal with transportation costs for commodities as a quantitative variable, admitting all the shades that can play a role (see Sec. 7.3). This necessitates the introduction of prices, since transportation costs can work out only through the prices of the products transported.

7.12 In this first section, we shall present the simplest approach to regional problems that can be applied in the absence of knowledge about the economic forces which determine the distribution of inputs of any kind over the regions of origin. This approach has been based on the method of input-output analysis and is due to Professor Hollis Chenery.[1] It consists in observing the existing distribution and assuming that this distribution remains the same with other absolute levels of production. We shall use this first model as an appropriate introduction to our subject since it enables us to leave prices out of consideration just as we did in Chaps. 4 and 5. We can thus concentrate on the purely quantitative variables which have to be introduced in a regional model before dealing with the price aspect. It will be assumed that there is complete mobility in all sectors except some *regional sectors;* that newly saved capital is freely mobile between sectors; and that population movements are irrelevant.

7.13 The variables of the model are

- ${}^{r}v^{h}$ production of commodity h in region r
- ${}^{r}v^{hh'}$ input of commodity h into sector h' for current production in region r
- ${}^{r}w^{hh'}$ investment input of commodity h into sector h' in region r

[1] "The Structure and Growth of the Italian Economy," chap. 5, Rome, 1953. See also L. N. Moses, The Stability of Interregional Trading Patterns and Input-Output Analysis, *Amer. Econ. Rev.*, vol. 45, p. 803, 1955; and W. W. Leontief and others, "Studies in the Structure of the American Economy," New York, 1953.

${}^{r}c^{h}$ consumption of commodity h in region r
${}^{r}e^{h}$ exports of commodity h from region r to foreign countries
${}^{r'r}x^{h}$ flow of commodity h from region r' to region r
${}^{r}y$ income of region r
${}^{r}s$ savings of region r

7.14 The relations of the model are

$$ {}^{r}w_{t}^{hh'} = \frac{{}^{r}\kappa^{hh'}}{\theta} \left({}^{r}v_{t+\theta}^{h'} - {}^{r}v_{t}^{h'} \right) \tag{7.14.1}$$

The possibility has been kept open that partial capital coefficients are different between regions, although it may seldom be possible to go into all details. For the sake of simplicity, no differences between gestation periods have been assumed, not even between sectors.

$$ \sum_{r} {}^{r}s = \sum_{r} \sum_{h} \sum_{h'} {}^{r}w^{hh'} \tag{7.14.2}$$

This equation assumes free mobility of newly formed capital.

$$ {}^{r}s = \sigma {}^{r}y \tag{7.14.3}$$

No difference in savings rate σ between the regions is made, although this could easily be done.

$$ {}^{r}y = \sum_{h} {}^{r}v^{h} - \sum_{h} \sum_{h'} {}^{r}v^{hh'} \tag{7.14.4}$$

$$ {}^{r}v^{h} = \sum_{r'} {}^{rr'}x^{h} \tag{7.14.5}$$

The intermediary variable ${}^{rr'}x^{h}$ is an easy tool of analysis in that it summarizes all commodity movements between regions irrespective of the destination given to them (consumption, current inputs, investment inputs, or exports); production in each region has then to be equal to the sum total of all shipments to all regions.

$$ \sum_{r'} {}^{r'r}x^{h} = {}^{r}\gamma^{h}({}^{r}y - {}^{r}s) + {}^{r}\bar{c}^{h} + \sum_{h'} {}^{r}v^{hh'} + \sum_{h'} {}^{r}w^{hh'} + {}^{r}e^{h} \tag{7.14.6}$$

All the *needs* of the region for good h have to be covered from the flow of good h into region r (including the region's own production as far as retained, ${}^{rr}x^{h}$).

$$ {}^{r}v^{hh'} = {}^{r}\varphi^{hh'} \, {}^{r}v^{h} \tag{7.14.7}$$

$$ {}^{r'r}x^{h} = {}^{r'r}\xi^{h} \sum_{r'} {}^{r'r}x^{h} \tag{7.14.9}$$

This equation is numbered (.9) since in the other models it has the same number. Equation (.8), being already needed in Chap. 6, but not used here, refers to price formation. The particular version of Eq. (.9) used here is the rigid one, in which ${}^{r'r}\xi^h$ are constants. They will have to obey the condition

$$\sum_{r'} {}^{r'r}\xi^h = 1 \tag{7.14.10}$$

For regional sectors $\quad {}^{r'r}\xi^h = 0 \quad$ for $r' \neq r$ (7.14.11)

and consequently ${}^{rr}\xi^h = 1$, that is, all needs are covered by production of the region itself.

The numbers of variables and of equations are, respectively, $2R + 3RH + 2RH^2 + R^2H$ and $1 + 2R + 2RH + 2RH^2 + R^2H$, indicating that there are $RH - 1$ degrees of freedom. Similarly to the model of Sec. 4.4, the variables ${}^re^h$ may be assumed to be given or to depend on some other variables, subject to the one condition that

$$\sum_r \sum_h {}^re^h = 0 \tag{7.14.12}$$

We should, however, add that for regional and national sectors the corresponding ${}^re^h$ all have to be zero, which restricts freedom. The remaining degrees of freedom may be used to maximize some policy aim, for example, national income.

7.15 As an illustration of the use of the model, this very example may again be taken up, as was done in Sec. 5.24. As before, savings s_0 can be invested in different sectors showing different capital coefficients and different contributions to national income per unit of product: φ^{0h}; in addition, there is a choice between regions now. In principle, the same problem arises, if all coefficients are constants: as a rule, there will be one sector in one region which is contributing most, per unit of investment, to future national income and in the absence of boundary conditions full specialization in that one sector would be the solution—with the proviso that a certain amount of investment will have to be used for regional and national sectors, the size of which is determined by consumption and other demands, depending on national income as a whole, directly and indirectly. Nevertheless, the approach is unrealistic, as was said of the approach in Sec. 5.24, and either boundary conditions or prices have to be introduced, as shown in the remainder of Chap. 5 and Chap. 6.

7.16 As a consequence of the subdivision into regions, our present model is already a little bit more realistic, as may be shown by the treatment of other policy problems in which the relation between regions plays a larger role.

If, for instance, the condition is added that incomes per head in the various regions must become as near equal as possible or rise by an equal percentage, the lopsided pattern first obtained will be corrected in a more realistic direction. Evidently the first problem, that of equalizing incomes per head, presupposes knowledge about the movement of population which may be either taken from other sources or assumed dependent on income differences. Both problems mentioned will tend to introduce into each region what is for that region the best industry, implying already a diversification of the production pattern.

A final example consists in the assumption that each region's savings are invested in that region. This changes the model since instead of Eq. (7.14.2) we now have R equations

$$^{r}s = \sum_{h} \sum_{h'} {}^{r}w^{hh'}$$

7.17 In order to remove the unrealistic features mentioned in Sec. 7.15, we may introduce prices, as in Chap. 6, and assume a relationship between volumes of production and prices, representing *world demand.* Assuming perfect markets within the country considered, the price of any commodity will be uniform in all regions. Our model can be easily generalized in this way. Prices would come in in the same way as in Chap. 6, since for them no regional differentiation is needed.

7.2. Transportation Costs Neglected; Prices Varying between Regions

7.21 The next simplest way to introduce prices into regional models is also similar to the way followed in Chap. 6, meaning that we still neglect transportation costs, as is usual in the theory of international trade. We shall assume now that prices are not only variables, but even may differ, for the same commodity, between regions. In other words we assume imperfect markets. This raises a further interesting question, namely, how demand reacts to the possibility of buying the same type of commodity at different prices. Usually in imperfect markets the commodities offered by different producers are supposed not to be identical; otherwise only one price could prevail. It will be assumed that the quantities bought from the various regions depend on the ratio of each price to the average price. The price at which each region supplies its product will be assumed to depend on the demand exerted in the region as well as in general for that particular product.

7.22 The variables of the model are

$^{r}v^{h}$ production of good h in region r
$^{r}v^{hh'}$ input of product h into current production in sector h' in region r
$^{r}w^{hh'}$ input of product h for investment in sector h' in region r
$^{r}c^{h}$ consumption of commodity h in region r
$^{r}e^{h}$ exports of commodity h by region r to foreign countries
$^{rr'}x^{h}$ flow of commodity h from region r to region r'
^{r}Y income of region r

^rS savings of region r
$^rp^h$ price of product h originating from region r
$^r\bar{p}^h$ average price paid for product h in region r

7.23 The relations constituting the model are

$$^rw^{hh'} = \frac{^r\kappa^{hh'}}{\theta}\left({}^rv^{h'}_{t+\theta} - {}^rv_t{}^{h'}\right) \tag{7.23.1}$$

$$\sum_r {}^rS = \sum_r \sum_h \sum_{h'} {}^rw^{hh'} \cdot {}^r\bar{p}^h \tag{7.23.2}$$

$$^rS = \sigma^rY \tag{7.23.3}$$

$$^rY = \sum_h {}^rp^h \left({}^rv^h - \sum_{h'} {}^r\varphi^{hh'}v^{h'}\right) \tag{7.23.4}$$

$$^rv^h = \sum_{r'} {}^{rr'}x^h \tag{7.23.5}$$

$$\sum_{r'} {}^{r'r}x^h = \frac{^r\gamma^h({}^rY - {}^rS)}{^r\bar{p}^h} + {}^r\bar{c}^h \frac{\sum_h {}^r\bar{p}^h}{^r\bar{p}^h} + \sum_{h'} {}^rv^{hh'} + \sum_{h'} {}^rw^{hh'} + {}^re^h \tag{7.23.6}$$

The shape of this equation corresponds to that given to Eq. (6.23.6); for the sake of simplicity, we have omitted the terms with $\gamma^{hh'}$ in the latter equation; these should run

$$\sum_{h'} {}^r\gamma^{hh'} \frac{^r\bar{p}^{h'}}{^r\bar{p}^h}$$

The omission means that we disregard price elasticities in consumer demand.

$$^rv^{hh'} = {}^r\varphi^{hh'} \cdot {}^rv^{h'} \tag{7.23.7}$$

$$^rp^h = {}^r\pi^h({}^rv^h)^{-\psi_1{}^h} \left(\sum_{r'} {}^{r'}v^h\right)^{-\psi_2{}^h} \tag{7.23.8}$$

As already mentioned, this is the equation for total demand; the price level of good h in region r is assumed to depend on demand exerted for region r's product as well as total demand for product h. The exponents are price flexibilities.

$$^{r'r}x^h = \left(\xi_0 - \xi_1 \frac{^{r'}p^h}{\sum_{r'} {}^{r'}p^h}\right) \sum_{r'} {}^{r'r}x^h \tag{7.23.9}$$

This is the relation also mentioned as determining the relative quantities bought in region r' as a function of the price ratio of region r' to the average of all prices for good h. Coefficients ξ_0 and ξ_1 must satisfy the condition[1]

$$R\xi_0 - \xi_1 = 1$$

$$^r\bar{p}^h = \frac{\Sigma^{r'r}x^h \cdot {}^{r'}p^h}{\Sigma^{r'r}x^h} \tag{7.23.10}$$

[1] Strictly speaking, there are also boundary conditions, namely, $^{r'r}x^h \geq 0$; we shall not pursue this issue further here, however.

7.24 With a model of this kind the problem of maximizing national income for year θ, with the side condition that savings S_0 in year 0 are given, can be treated in a way similar to the one set out in Chap. 6. Income for the economy as a whole can be expressed again as a function of all ${}^r v^h$, since prices ${}^r p^h$ can be so expressed with the aid of (7.23.8). It will depend to a high degree on the nature of the functions, that is, the coefficients and exponents in (7.23.8), whether solutions are obtained obeying the boundary conditions, but the chances are better than they would be without the introduction of prices.

Clearly there are other problems which can be treated with the present model, for example, those mentioned in Sec. 7.16.

7.3. Static Models with Transportation Costs

7.31 In this section we present two models with transportation costs, the element so far neglected. The models are of a very simple, static type and focus on the phenomena implied by the introduction of transportation costs.[1] In the next section the development planning model, with transportation costs, will be taken up again.

Transportation costs arise from the movement of goods between geographically separated regions or centers. Generally, the costs per unit of product depend on the distance between the regions, the means of transportation used (rail, road, water), and the nature of the goods transported. Costs may be assumed proportional to distance, but when we want to distinguish between the fixed costs, including those of loading and unloading, and the variable costs, they are not. For long distances, however, variable costs prevail. Furthermore, transportation costs can be an absolute markup on the producer's price or a proportional one. An ad valorem tariff is an example of the latter case. Here we shall make the assumption of proportionality, but, in principle, it is not difficult to introduce alternative assumptions.

The models of this section subdivide the economy into industries and regions. The impact which transportation costs can have on the economy is further given its full weight by assuming that both demand and supply are influenced by prices. Therefore, the models distinguish supply and demand functions for each product in each region as functions of the relevant prices and incomes.

Two alternative assumptions can be made with regard to the reactions of demand to price changes.

1. The demand will fully shift to the cheapest supplier if one of the

[1] J. Tinbergen, The Appraisal of Road Construction: Two Calculation Schemes, *Rev. Econ. Stat.*, vol. 39, p. 241, August, 1957.

supply prices changes (assumption of infinite substitution between competitors).

2. The demand will only partly shift to cheaper suppliers (assumption of finite elasticity of substitution between competitors).

Two different models correspond to these two cases. The problem to be solved with these models is to estimate the consequences of a change in transportation costs. Such a change may be due to the construction or improvement of roads. The present models, therefore, may be used in the appraisal of road construction. In such a case the change in the national product caused by the decrease in transportation costs may be considered as a measure of the national returns of the project.

We discuss first a model based on the assumption of an infinite substitution elasticity in demand.

7.32 The variables of the model are

${}^{rr'}v^h$ volume of product h transported from region r to region r'
${}^{rr'}V^h$ value of ${}^{rr'}v^h$ in region r'
${}^{r}p^h$ price of product h in production region r

7.33 The relationships of the model are the following.

$$ {}^{rr'}V^h = {}^{rr'}v^h \cdot {}^{r}p^h \cdot {}^{rr'}T^h \tag{7.33.1} $$

These equations define the value of ${}^{rr'}v^h$ as the price at the delivery region r', that is, inclusive of transportation costs. The *transportation coefficients* ${}^{rr'}T^h$ are given constants; they are equal to 1 for $r = r'$.

If r supplies product h to r'

$$ {}^{rr'}V^h = {}^{r'}\xi^h \sum_{h'} \sum_{r''} {}^{r'r''}V^{h'} \tag{7.33.2} $$

If r'' does not supply product h to r'

$$ {}^{r''r'}V^h = 0 \tag{7.33.3} $$

These two sets of equations (.2) and (.3) represent expenditure equations. In (.2) the expression $\Sigma\Sigma^{r'r''}V^{h'}$ represents the income of r', and the expenditure on product h is a constant fraction ${}^{r'}\xi^h$ of this income. The propensities to spend ξ have to fulfill the condition $\sum_h {}^{r'}\xi^h = 1$, since we are considering a static model. The equations (.2) are valid only for the demand for product h from the region which has the lowest supply price in r'. In (.3), r'' indicates the regions not delivering to r'.

$$ {}^{r}p^h \sum_{r'} {}^{rr'}v^h = {}^{r}\bar{\sigma}^h \cdot {}^{r}p^h - {}^{r}\sigma^h \sum_{h' \neq h} {}^{r'}p^{h'} \cdot {}^{r'r}T^{h'} \tag{7.33.4} $$

In these supply equations the expression at the left-hand side represents the production value of product h supplied by region r to other regions, including itself. At the right-hand side ${}^{r}\bar{\sigma}^{h}$ stands for the capacity limit, and ${}^{r}\sigma^{h}$ is a coefficient related to the supply elasticity. The equation assumes the quantity supplied to be a hyperbolic function of the price relation ${}^{r}p^{h}/\left(\sum_{h' \neq h} {}^{r'}p^{h'} \cdot {}^{r'r}T^{h'}\right)$. The denominator of this relation can be considered to express in a rough way the costs of producing product h in r.

7.34 The use to be made of the model is to estimate what the effect of a change in one (or more) of the transportation coefficients will be. As will be understood from the assumption of an infinite substitution elasticity, such a change affects not only the prices and, consequently, the quantities supplied and demanded, but also the pattern of commodity flows between the regions. For example, region r' buying product h from r may shift its demand to region r'', after a reduction of the transportation costs for product h between r' and r''. This feature of the model makes no easy solution possible. First, a provisional choice has to be made as to which are the cheapest supplying regions for each product, and on the basis of this choice it has to be tested by solving the model whether each region is actually buying from the cheapest supplier. If this test is not satisfied, a new choice has to be made, etc. Only by trial and error can we find the correct solution.[1]

7.35 The second model in this section is based on the assumption of a finite substitution elasticity. If the supply price of product h from region r' in r falls below the price of h originating from r'', the demand will only partly shift from r'' to r'. Thus, the same product may be purchased by r from more than one region. Clearly, this will happen only in the case of an imperfect market or, in other words, in the case of product differentiation.

A second assumption of this model is that each region produces one product only. This assumption makes a separate index for the product superfluous and, accordingly, we simplify the notation.

- ${}^{rr'}v$ volume of the product produced in r and transported to r'
- ${}^{rr'}V$ value of ${}^{rr'}v$ at the price in r'
- p^{r} price of the product produced by r in the production region

7.36 The equations of the model are the following.

$$ {}^{rr'}V = {}^{rr'}v p^{r} \cdot {}^{rr'}T \tag{7.36.1} $$

$$ {}^{rr'}V = {}^{r'}\bar{\eta}^{r} \sum_{r''} {}^{r'r''}V - \eta^{r'} p^{r} \cdot {}^{rr'}T + \frac{\eta^{r'}}{n-1} \sum_{r'' \neq r} p^{r''} \cdot {}^{r''r'}T \tag{7.36.2} $$

In these expenditure equations $\sum_{r''} V^{r'r''}$ measures the income of region r',

[1] For a numerical example, see *ibid.*

and ${}^{r'}\bar{\eta}^{r}$ represents the propensity to spend on the product from r by region r'. Thus, the first term on the right-hand side of the equations represents the influence of the income of region r' on its expenditures on the product of region r. The two other expressions indicate the influence on the expenditures of the price of the product purchased and of the prices of the other products purchased by region r', respectively. These last two influences are formulated in such a way that they cancel out when the expenditures of one region on the products of all regions are added up. On the assumption that $\sum_{r} {}^{r'}\bar{\eta}^{r} = 1$, the condition of a static model is fulfilled: the income of each region is fully spent.

$$p^{r} \sum_{r'} {}^{rr'}v = \bar{\rho}^{r}p^{r} - \rho^{r} \sum_{r' \neq r} p^{r'} \cdot {}^{r'r}T \tag{7.36.3}$$

These supply equations do not differ from those of the first model (Sec. 7.33).

7.37 The solution of this model is simpler than that of the first because the location of the supplying regions does not shift after a change in the transportation costs. The solution proceeds along the following lines. The expenditures of all regions together on the product of one region r can be derived from the demand functions and expressed as a function of the prices of all products and the total income of the regions, which can be considered as given. By taking account of the transportation costs, the producer's value can be derived from the expenditures on r. This value should be equal to the producer's value as given by the supply function for r. Thus, by equating for each product the producer's value as derived from the demand and from the supply side, we find a set of linear equations with the prices as the only unknowns, which enables us to solve, first, the prices and, next, the values and the volumes. Numerical examples are given elsewhere.[1]

7.4. Development Model with Transportation Costs

7.41 The concepts and relations described in Sec. 7.3, in order to deal with transportation costs and their impact on the economy, will now be used in a model for development planning in many sectors and regions. As before, the model will be an input-output model; it will be possible to introduce elements of linear programming for such sectors where this makes sense. The model will be a further generalization of the one shown in Sec. 7.2.

[1] See *ibid.* and H. C. Bos and L. M. Koyck, The Appraisal of Road Construction Projects: A Practical Example, *Rev. Econ. Stat.*, vol. 43, no. 1, pp. 13–20, February, 1961.

We will consider transportation as a separate sector, which we give the index $h = 1$. Like other sectors, this sector will have its own inputs for current production as well as for investment. Furthermore, transportation will be treated as a regional sector in that all the transportation of goods originating from region r is considered to be produced in that region, that is, ${}^{r'r}x^1 = 0$ for $r' \neq r$ and ${}^{rr}x^1 = {}^{r}v^1$, as well as ${}^{r}e^1 = 0$. It will be assumed, however, that the inputs of transportation services into other sectors are not following the usual input-output schedule of proportionality. It will rather be assumed that all ${}^{r}\varphi^{1h} = {}^{r}\kappa^{1h} = 0$ and that the value of transportation services rendered by region r is equal to

$$
{}^{rr}x_t^1 \cdot {}^{r}p_t^1 = \sum_h \sum_{r'} {}^{rr'}x_t^h \cdot {}^{r}p_t^h({}^{rr'}T^h - 1) + {}^{r}\gamma^1({}^{r}Y - {}^{r}S) + {}^{r}\bar{c}^1 \sum_h {}^{r}\bar{p}^h \qquad (7.41.1)
$$

On the right-hand side we first have the value increase due to transportation of all flows ${}^{rr'}x_t^h$ of goods transported from sector r to other sectors, ${}^{r}p_t^h$ being the price of these goods in region r and ${}^{r}p_t^h \cdot {}^{rr'}T^h$ their price in region r'. The second and third term on the right-hand side represent consumers' demand for transportation. Equation (7.41.1) rests on the assumption already mentioned that all transports starting in sector r are counted as transportation services produced in sector r. One could of course have followed different principles of computation here.

With regard to the distribution of demand exerted by any sector r over the sectors of origin, we make the same assumption as was made in Sec. 7.2. This corresponds to what was called in Sec. 7.3 the method of *finite elasticities of substitution.*

7.42 The variables of the model are

${}^{r}v_t^h$	production of commodity h in region r
${}^{r}v_t^{hh'}$	input of product h into current production of sector h' in region r
${}^{r}w_t^{hh'}$	input of product h for investment in sector h' in region r
${}^{r}c_t^h$	consumption of commodity h in region r
${}^{r}e_t^h$	exports of commodity h from region r to foreign countries
${}^{rr'}x_t^h$	flow of commodity h from region r to region r'
${}^{r}Y_t$	income of region r
${}^{r}S_t$	savings of region r
${}^{r}p_t^h$	price in region r of product h originating in region r
${}^{r}p_t^h \cdot {}^{rr'}T_t^h$	price in region r' of product h originating in region r
${}^{r}\bar{p}_t^h$	average price paid for product h in region r

All variables refer to period t.

7.43 The relations of this model are

$$ {}^r w_t^{hh'} = \frac{{}^r\kappa^{hh'}}{\theta} \left({}^r v_{t+\theta}^{h'} - {}^r v_t^{h'}\right) \qquad (7.43.1) $$

$$ \sum_r {}^r S_t = \sum_r \sum_h \sum_{h'} {}^r w_t^{hh'} \cdot {}^r \bar{p}_t^h \qquad (7.43.2) $$

$$ {}^r S_t = \sigma^r Y_t \qquad (7.43.3) $$

$$ {}^r Y_t = \sum_h {}^r p_t^h \left({}^r v_t^h - \sum_{h'} {}^r \varphi^{hh'} \cdot {}^r v_t^{h'}\right) \qquad (7.43.4) $$

$$ {}^r v_t^h = \sum_{r'} {}^{rr'} x_t^h \qquad (7.43.5) $$

$$ {}^{rr} x_t^1 \cdot {}^r p_t^1 = \sum_h \sum_{r'} {}^{rr'} x_t^h \cdot {}^r p_t^h \left({}^{rr'} T_t^h - 1\right) + {}^r\gamma^1 ({}^r Y - {}^r S) + {}^r \bar{c}^1 \sum_h {}^r \bar{p}^h \qquad (7.43.6') $$

$$ \sum_{r'} {}^{r'r} x_t^h = \frac{{}^r\gamma^h ({}^r Y_t - {}^r S_t)}{{}^r \bar{p}_t^h} + {}^r \bar{c}^h \frac{\sum_h {}^r \bar{p}_t^h}{{}^r \bar{p}_t^h} + \sum_{h'} {}^r v_t^{hh'} + \sum_{h'} {}^r w_t^{hh'} + {}^r e^h \qquad h = 2, \ldots, H \qquad (7.43.6'') $$

As before, we have neglected price elasticities of consumer demand. If we do not want to neglect them, a term should be added: $\sum_{h'} {}^r\gamma^{hh'} \frac{{}^r \bar{p}_t^{h'}}{{}^r \bar{p}_t^h}$.

$$ {}^r v_t^{hh'} = {}^r \varphi^{hh'} \cdot {}^r v_t^{h'} \qquad (7.43.7) $$

$$ {}^r p_t^h = {}^r \pi^h ({}^r v_t^h)^{-\psi_1^h} \Big(\sum_{r'} {}^{r'} v_t^h\Big)^{-\psi_2^h} \qquad (7.43.8) $$

$$ {}^{r'r} x_t^1 = 0 \qquad \text{for } r' \neq r \qquad (7.43.9') $$

$$ {}^{r'r} x_t^h = \left(\xi_0 - \xi_1 \frac{{}^{r'} p_t^h \cdot {}^{r'r} T_t^h}{\sum_{r'} {}^{r'} p_t^h \cdot {}^{r'r} T_t^h}\right) \sum_{r'} {}^{r'r} x_t^h \qquad h = 2, \ldots, H \qquad (7.43.9'') $$

$$ {}^r \bar{p}_t^h = \frac{\sum_{r'} {}^{r'r} x_t^h \cdot {}^{r'} p_t^h \cdot {}^{r'r} T_t^h}{\sum_{r'} {}^{r'r} x_t^h} \qquad (7.43.10) $$

For $h = 1$ we take ${}^r \bar{p}_t^1 = {}^r p_t^1$.

7.44 The model has become more complicated than those discussed in Chap. 6; it has become necessary to distinguish between producers' price ${}^r p^h$ and consumers' price ${}^r \bar{p}^h$ for the same commodity h in the same region r. The most important planning problem which must be solved, the one discussed in Sec. 6.2, becomes more complicated as a consequence. We shall discuss its solution in this section. As before, we consider as given, at a time t, the production capacities of all sectors in all regions, and we assume that they are fully used, meaning that all ${}^{r}v_t{}^h$ are known. Consequently also the ${}^{r}p_t{}^h$ are known from Eq. (7.43.8), the ${}^{r}v_t{}^{hh'}$ from (7.43.7), and ${}^{r}Y_t$ and ${}^{r}S_t$ from Eqs. (7.43.4) and (7.43.3). Our planning problem is to determine ${}^{r}v_t{}^{hh'}$, ${}^{r}w_t{}^{hh'}$, ${}^{rr'}x_t{}^h$, ${}^{r}e^h$, and we shall need the ${}^{r}\bar{p}_t{}^h$ for this purpose.

As before, we must know the ${}^{r}v_{t+\theta}^h$ in order to be able to determine the unknowns just enumerated, since the ${}^{r}w_t{}^{hh'}$ depend on them by virtue of (7.43.1). In Sec. 6.2, we determined the ${}^{r}v_{t+\theta}^h$ from a maximization of $Y_{t+\theta}$, given total savings σY_t at time t. It is this part of the problem which has now become more complicated, since the side condition (7.43.2), under which this maximization of $Y_{t+\theta}$ has to be carried out, contains the unknown ${}^{r}\bar{p}_t{}^h$.

The exact method of solution consists in expressing, with the aid of Eqs. (7.43.1), (7.43.5), (7.43.9), and (7.43.10), the ${}^{r}\bar{p}_t{}^h$ and the other unknowns ${}^{r}w_t{}^{hh'}$ and ${}^{rr'}x_t{}^h$ in terms of ${}^{r}v_{t+\theta}^h$ (and ${}^{r}v_t{}^h$) and in finding the side condition (7.43.2) imposed on the ${}^{r}v_{t+\theta}^h$. From the maximization of $Y_{t+\theta}$, under this latter side condition, the ${}^{r}v_{t+\theta}^h$ must be determined. Since the side condition is no longer linear, this will be a cumbersome process.

For practical purposes it may be better to assume tentative values for ${}^{r}\bar{p}_t{}^h$ in side condition (7.43.2), which reduces the problem to the simple shape it took in Sec. 6.2. This will lead to provisional values of ${}^{r}V_{t+\theta}^h$.

After the values of ${}^{r}v_{t+\theta}^h$ have been found, the remaining unknowns can be found, that is, the unknowns ${}^{r}\bar{p}_t{}^h$, ${}^{r}w_t{}^{hh'}$, ${}^{rr'}x_t{}^h$, and ${}^{r}e_t{}^h$.

In case the tentative values assumed for ${}^{r}\bar{p}_t{}^h$ do not coincide with the ones just found, a second round of calculations will have to be started on the basis of the second approximations found for ${}^{r}\bar{p}_t{}^h$; strictly speaking, it should be proved that such an iteration process will converge.

It should be added that again the values for ${}^{r}e_t{}^h$ will obey a condition which now runs $\sum_r \sum_h {}^{r}e_t{}^h \cdot {}^{r}\bar{p}_t{}^h = 0$.

Chapter 8

SOME CRITICAL AND CONCLUDING REMARKS

8.1. Some Critical Remarks on the Present State of the Discipline

8.11 The subject of development programming has attracted the interest of a number of authors these last ten years, and a considerable body of knowledge and insight have come into existence. Since the discipline is a young one, it is the playground of all sorts of pioneering, and it could not be otherwise. Some first-rank scientists of different denomination have given thought to the subject matter, among them several not mainly interested in economic problems. The subject also has been one of intensive political controversy. For all these reasons, sometimes very unorthodox ideas have been launched, so much so that the authors, though not themselves feeling orthodox, think that some critical remarks on a few of these ideas are in order. They want to present these remarks in all modesty, being aware of the big role unorthodox approaches sometimes have to play and being aware also of the restricted tools they themselves handle. The general attitude the authors take in this section is the attitude of the economist trying to test the economic soundness of some of the ideas they criticize. They are aware of the autonomous rights of politicians, on the one hand, to choose their aims and of mathematicians, on the other hand, to choose their methods of analysis.

8.12 To begin with, some critical remarks will be made on the aims assumed for development programming, while remembering the autonomy of politicians in this field.

1. Aims are often not very clearly specified. This applies to the economic variables representing the aims as well as to the timing of these

variables. As has been shown in Sec. 3.5, it can make a tremendous difference whether a development plan aims at maximum consumption five, ten, or twenty years from the start of the plan. The nature of the variables representing the aims is very often of a derived nature, and it is not clear whether the relationship between the ultimate aim and the derived aim is very clear to those setting the aims. Is income the aim, or consumption, or the satisfaction derived from consumption? This is only one example of many other conceivable questions that are often not answered. The number of aims is another case in point.

2. An extremely important example of an aim which plays a preponderant role in a number of countries is the alleged priority given to heavy industry. This also can be understood only as a derived aim, not an autonomous one. It is highly desirable that this relationship be discussed more openly in order to understand what the real choice—in terms of ultimate aims—amounts to.

3. A similar question has to be put with regard to the degree of autarchy aimed at by many programmers from the political angle. There is hardly another example to be found where the relationship between the practical aim set and the ultimate aim behind it is so much one of partly antiquated links, links valid only in a previous era.

4. An important group of scientific workers in the field likes to assume that the relative importance the population or their representatives attach to the various aims of a program of development is constant, independently of the level of satisfaction reached. We are hinting, of course, at the assumption of a linear maximand made in linear programming. This seems to us an unhappy way of molding reality to the shape of a simple theory.

5. A famous example of something similar is the assumption that a given, fixed composition of the stock of capital goods is the aim of development policy. This aim has been assumed by a number of authors, who are dealing, it seems, with what may be called a *prestage* to balanced growth. The economic future, in this context, consists of two stages, of which the second is the one of balanced growth. During the first stage, a number of bottlenecks have to be overcome in order that the subsequent process may be one of balanced development. If this is the approach these authors have in mind, it might be useful to state it explicitly.

Most of the processes dealt with in this book are meant to be models for balanced growth, that is, for the second stage just mentioned. This does not preclude the possibility of the existence of bottlenecks even during such a process. To a certain extent it is a question of taste whether factors of a scarce nature are or are not called bottlenecks. The clearest example in this book of the prestage mentioned is what has here been called the adaptation process (see Sec. 4.2).

8.13 Next, some critical remarks may be made with regard to the assumptions made about the structure of the economy.

1. The same lack of clarity in stating explicitly the aims of development policy can be found in the realm of the means of that policy. The important question of what and how many means can be handled is often passed by in complete silence. A more explicit and a more precise discussion would contribute not only to the efficiency of planning but even to more mutual understanding between the representatives of politically opposed groups.

2. In some famous purely scientific analyses of the process of development assumptions are made with respect to the behavior of consumption which really are too simple. One is the assumption that consumption over time per unit of labor input is constant; the other is that consumption is autonomous.

3. Equally oversimplified is the assumption that, on the production side, there are only two, rather distinct, techniques available in the economy as a whole, not themselves changing over time.

4. Similarly the time structure is also much too much simplified in models in which a uniform gestation period is assumed to exist for all investment processes.

5. A hypothesis which has not been very explicitly formulated but actually is at the basis of a famous scientific and political controversy—the one about the choice of technology—is the assumption that investment is mainly financed out of profits. This hypothesis neglects the possibility of financing investment out of indirect taxes, and this neglect means a heavy qualification of the devices on technology formulated by the advocates of the "most advanced technology."

6. A general drawback to the use of linear models is the necessity to introduce a large number of boundary conditions, some of which are of a very arbitrary character. Especially boundary conditions on the volume of sales—national or international—of a given commodity are a really too crude representation of the law of demand.

8.14 Finally some critical remarks may be made on the solutions of some of the major problems of development programming.

1. There is too little awareness of the very unsatisfactory state of our insight into the main problem: the problem of the optimum rate of development (see Sec. 2.4). This means that (*a*) more efforts should be devoted to a solution of this problem and (*b*) practical planning should be undertaken in the awareness that the decision on the rate of development cannot be very precise and for that reason had better be taken first, starting more precise work after this choice has been made.

2. A practical development policy cannot be carried out without some

instruments for short-term adaptations of the economy to quick changes in data; but these adaptations cannot be studied with the aid of existing long-term planning models, since the short-term solutions of the movements of these models are unreliable (see Sec. 4.66). It is necessary and possible to study short-term movements with the aid of models of another type.

3. Even with a perfect regulation of short-term disturbances, it is not always possible suddenly to change the pattern of long-term development if that is desired. Such changes may require a period of adaptation of the volumes of specific capital goods, and this period may be considerable.

8.2. Some Practical Suggestions

In conclusion, some practical suggestions may be made regarding the computation of a development program for a national economy over a given planning period. The following stages in such a computation seem to make sense.

1. The most desirable general rate of development, that is, the rate of increase in national income at constant internal prices, is estimated with the aid of a simple macromodel, using provisional data on the capital coefficient for the nation as a whole and on foreign investment to be expected. The estimate must be based on an intuitive comparison between future advantages and present disadvantages of an increase in saving.

2. A choice is made on the number and exact definition of sectors to be considered.

3. Home demand for finished products is estimated for all years of the planning periods on the basis of the projection of income and investment, assuming no structural changes.

4. Demand for existing export products is estimated for all years of the planning period, assuming no price changes.

5. Current demand for intermediate products—as far as represented in the choice of sectors—is estimated on the basis of final demands computed under stages 3 and 4. Among these are imports.

6. Contributions to the national product to be obtained from a unit of new investment in each of the sectors and of possible new sectors are estimated, partly on the basis of data on individual projects, partly on the basis of general knowledge on learning curves and on the influence of the size of an enterprise on its costs.

7. If exports found under stage 4 fall short of imports found under stage 5 by an amount surpassing expected capital imports, new exports or import-replacing production volumes are estimated in the sectors contributing most (per unit of new investment) to national product so as to

equilibrate the balance of payments. Sectors with high comparative advantages may even be expanded to such an extent that the corresponding prices fall, the consequences of which must then be estimated.

8. Similar variations in the production program may be envisaged in order to fulfill other aims of development policy, such as employment or distribution objectives.

9. With the aid of sector capital coefficients, or an "investment input matrix," the investment needs may now be specified in a more precise way, according to the supplying sectors and on the basis of gestation lags.

10. If total investments needed each year, calculated under stage 9, are deviating too much from the investment volumes assumed under stage 1, this latter calculation can now be corrected and all the subsequent estimates revised.

11. The investment program may now be "filled" with individual projects, taken in the order of attractiveness as found under stage 6.

The reader will understand that the above suggestions are based on the techniques developed in the preceding chapters and models and that the model discussed in Sec. 6.2 will be of considerable help. Practical programming will often have to go beyond this model, however, or at least supplement it with partial research. This applies above all to the computations in stages 6, 7, and 8. Sometimes elements as discussed in Secs. 5.4 to 5.6 or 6.3 may be inserted in such a "partial" way, that is, in one sector or a few sectors to which these elements apply more particularly.

The *splitting up* of a national program into regional programs may be the next task for the development planner. Here the distance between practical possibilities and theoretical models is considerable still. The statistical data needed for a model in which transportation costs are fully playing their role are hardly available. To begin with, a distinction between *regional* sectors and sectors the products of which can move to other regions can be made. Next, differences in production costs between regions can be ascertained. Thus, some regional distribution of production can be made without having recourse to details about transportation costs. As a third step, transportation costs can be brought into the picture for such sectors as show high—but not prohibitive—transportation costs. This seems to be the most practical approach to regional planning at the moment. Further refinements, along the lines of the model discussed in Sec. 7.4, may be the next step. Here, however, we are clearly on academic rather than practical ground.

Appendix

SYMBOLS USED

General Remarks on Symbols

Lower index as a rule indicates time period to which variable refers.

Upper index h or h' indicates sector (industry); in some cases upper index 1, 2 indicates process of production or geographical sector. Symbols with one index only are given without index in the following list; thus, meaning of v^h can be found under v, etc. Symbols with two indexes, for example, $v^{hh'}$, have been mentioned separately.

Money values are indicated by capital letters, usually but not always corresponding to symbols for volume variables. Greek symbols often are corresponding coefficients (for example, x, X, ξ; s, S, σ; etc.). Dot on top of symbol indicates derivative with regard to time: $\dot{c} = dc/dt$, etc.

List of Symbols

I. Alphabetical order of definitions[1]

Allocation of investment coefficient, Mahalanobis, Λ
Balance-of-payments deficit, F
Capital, in accounting sector, $\tilde{k}$
  in existence, k^0
  in nonaccounting sector, $\bar{k}$
  in use, k, K
Capital exponent in Douglas production function, μ
Capital-income ratio, gross, κ'
  net, κ
Capital supply flexibility, β

[1] Some symbols which do not have generally used names have been included only in list II below.

Growth rate, of efficiency, ϵ
  of population, π
  of production, ω
Horizon, T
Import content, ι
Imports, i, I
Income, national, y, Y
Index, sector, h, H (maximum)
Interest rate, m
  accounting, m'
Interindustry deliveries, current, $v^{hh'}$, $V^{hh'}$
Interindustry delivery coefficient, current, $\varphi^{hh'}$
  investment, $\kappa^{hh'}$
Interindustry investment, $w^{hh'}$, $W^{hh'}$
Investment coefficient, $\kappa^{hh'}$
  finished, j', J'
  gross, j^G, J^G
  net, j, J
  replacement, r, R
Labor-capital ratio, without accounting prices, Φ_0
  in accounting sector, Φ_1
Labor exponent, Douglas production function, λ
    rate of change, λ'
Labor productivity, g
Labor supply flexibility, α
Leontief coefficients, current, $\varphi^{hh'}$
  investment, $\kappa^{hh'}$
Lifetime of investment goods, Θ
Marginal utility, u
  flexibility, v
National expenditure, x, X
National income, y, Y
Output-capital ratio, ζ
Population, P
  growth rate, π
Price capital stock, q'
Price consumption, p^c
Price exports, p^e
Price gross product, p
Price imports, p^i
Price investment, q
Price national expenditure, p^x

Price national income, p^y
Price product, h, p^h
Product, gross, v
Production, rate of growth, ω
Productivity, labor, g
Propensity, to consume, γ
  of region r to buy good h in region r', ${}^{rr}\xi^h$
  to spend, ξ
Region index, r, R (maximum)
Repayment period, τ
Replacement investment, r, R
Savings, s, S
  rate, σ
Sector index, h, H (maximum)
Spend, propensity to, ξ
Supply coefficient, product, ρ
Supply flexibility, capital, β
  labor, α
Taxes, G
Time, t
  integration variable, t'
Transportation coefficient, ${}^{r'r}T^h$
Utility, marginal, u
    flexibility of, v
  total, U
Wage rate, l
  accounting, l'
  desired, l^0
    rate of growth, Ω

II. Alphabetical order of symbols—Latin[1]

a	Employment	A	(*see* Greek list)
$\tilde{a}$	Employment in accounting sector		
$\bar{a}$	Employment in non-accounting sector		
b	*Volume of equipment	B	(*see* Greek list)
c	Consumption volume; $c' = c - \bar{c}$	C	Value

[1] Asterisk * indicates stock variable.

	$\tilde{c}$ Total consumption in period $0 \leq t \leq T$		
	$\tilde{c}^h$ Constant in Engel function		
	$\bar{c}$ Subsistence minimum		
	c^F Consumption of French workers		
	c^m Saturation level		
d	Depreciation allowances, volume	D	Value
e	Exports, volume[1]	E	Value
	$\bar{e}_1^h$ Constant in function describing time pattern of e^h		
f	Foreign exchange rate	F	Deficit on balance of payments
g	Labor productivity	G	Taxes
h	Sector index	H	Maximum value of sector index
			H^E Number of export items
i	Imports, volume	I	Value
j	Investment, net, volume	J	Value
j'	Investment, finished, volume	J'	Value
j^G	Investment, gross, volume	J^G	Value
k	*Capital stock volume, in use	K	*Value
	$\tilde{k}$ Capital in accounting sector		
	$\bar{k}$ Capital in non-accounting sector		
	k^0 Capital stock volume, in existence		
l	Wage rate		
	l^0 Desired wage rate		
	l' Accounting wage rate		
m	Interest rate	M	*Foreign debt
	m' Accounting interest rate		
	$\bar{m}$ Discount rate		

[1] Of course, e is also used for base natural logarithms.

p	Price index of gross product[1]	P	*Population
	p^h Price index of product h		
q	Price index of investment goods		
	q' Price index of capital stock		
r	Replacement investment, volume	R	Number of regions
	As an index: region		
s	Savings, volume	S	Value
t	Time	T	Horizon
	t' Time as integration variable	${}^{r'r}T$	Transportation coefficient
	t'', t''' Integration variable depending on t'		
u	Marginal utility	U	Total utility
v	Volume of gross product	V	Value
	$\bar{v}^h$, $\bar{v}_0{}^h$, $\bar{v}_{0h}{}^h$ Constants in functions describing time path of $v_t{}^h$		
	$v^{hh'}$ Interindustry deliveries, current		
$w^{hh'}$	Interindustry deliveries for investment purposes	$W^{hh'}$	Value
x	National expenditure, volume	X	Value
	${}^{rr'}x^h$ Quantity of good h supplied by region r to region r'		
y	National income, volume	Y	Value
	$y' = y - \bar{c}$		
	$\bar{y}$ Constant in Sec. 2.4		

III. Alphabetical order of symbols—Greek

α	Supply flexibility of labor	A	$c^m/\bar{c}$ (Sec. 2.4)
β	Supply flexibility of capital	B	Constant in consumption time path (Sec. 2.4)

[1] Upper index, when applied, indicates corresponding volume (c, i, e, x, y).

γ	Propensity to consume $\gamma^{hh'}$ Other constants appearing in consumption function	Γ	Constant in Douglas production function
δ	Rate of depreciation $\delta' = 1 - \delta$	Δ	Finite increase in variable it precedes
ϵ	Rate of growth of efficiency		
ζ	Output-capital ratio $\zeta^{hh'}$ Partial output-capital ratio		
η	Elasticity (or coefficient) of demand		
θ	Gestation period	Θ	Lifetime of investment goods
ι	Import content of product		
κ	Capital-output ratio, net		
κ'	Capital-output ratio, gross $\kappa^{hh'}$ Partial capital-output ratio		
λ	Labor exponent in Douglas production function λ' Rate of change of λ	Λ	Mahalanobis allocation of investment coefficient
μ	Capital exponent in Douglas production function		
ξ	Propensity to spend ${}^{r'r}\xi^h$ Propensity of region r to buy good h in region r' ξ_0, ξ_1 Constants in this propensity, when dependent on relative prices	Ξ	Mahalanobis employment coefficient
π	Rate of growth of population		
ρ	Elasticity of supply		
σ	Rate of savings		

τ	Period of repayment		
υ	Flexibility of marginal utility		
$\varphi^{hh'}$	Current Leontief coefficients	Φ_0	Labor-capital ratio without accounting prices
$\bar{\chi}, \chi^{hh'}$	Constants in function describing time path of v_t^h	Φ_1	Labor-capital ratio in accounting sector
ψ	Price flexibility of demand		
ω	Rate of growth of production	Ω	Rate of increase in desired wage rate

BIBLIOGRAPHY

Banerji, H.: Technical Progress and the Process of Economic Development, *NUFFIC*, The Hague, 1956.

Baumol, William J.: "Economic Dynamics," New York, 1959.

Bos, H. C., and L. M. Koyck: The Appraisal of Investments in Road Projects; A Practical Example, *Rev. Econ. Stat.*, vol. 43, no. 1, pp. 13–20, February, 1961.

Chenery, Hollis B.: Development Policies and Programmes, *Econ. Bull. (Latin America)*, vol. 3, p. 51, 1958.

——— and Paul C. Clark: "Interindustry Economics," New York, 1959.

——— and Kenneth S. Kretschmer: Resource Allocation for Economic Development, *Econometrica*, vol. 24, no. 4, p. 365, 1956.

Domar, Evsey D.: "Essays on the Theory of Economic Growth," New York, 1957.

Dorfman, R., P. A. Samuelson, and R. M. Solow: "Linear Programming and Economic Analysis," New York, 1958.

Harrod, R. F.: "Towards a Dynamic Economics," London, 1948.

Kaldor, Nicholas: Capital Accumulation and Economic Growth, Corfu Meeting, International Economic Association (extended mimeographed version), 1958.

Leontief, Wassily W.: "The Structure of the American Economy, 1919–1939," New York, 1951.

———, ed.: "Studies in the Structure of the American Economy," New York, 1953.

Samuelson, P. A. and R. M. Solow: A Complete Capital Model Involving Heterogeneous Capital Goods, *Quart. J. Econ.*, vol. 70, p. 537, 1956.

Sandee, J.: "A Demonstration Planning Model for India," Calcutta, 1960.

Solow, Robert M.: A Contribution to the Theory of Economic Growth, *Quart. J. Econ.*, vol. 70, p. 65, 1956.

Tinbergen, J.: "Economic Policy: Principles and Design," Amsterdam, 1956.

———: "The Design of Development," Baltimore, 1958.

———: "Selected Papers," Amsterdam, 1959.

Verdoorn, P. J.: Complementarity and Long-range Projections, *Econometrica*, vol. 24, no. 4, p. 429, 1956.

INDEX